LOVE

Having devoted herself to her career, Samantha was on the verge of a collapse and had been warned to rest. So she took herself off to a quiet cottage in Cornwall—and promptly fell in love with Bart Jackson, who had no time for career girls and thought she was a quiet little homebody . . .

CINDERELLA IN MINK

Nicola Rosten was used to the flattery and deference accorded to a very wealthly woman. Yet Barnaby Grayson mistook her for a down-and-out and set her to work in the kitchen. Should she tell him the truth? And how would he react?

RENT A WIFE

To help a sick friend, Natalie had offered to hold the fort at her marriage bureau—a kind gesture that had unexpected, and unfortunate, repercussions, when the first person she met there was Miles Denton, furiously angry, and did she but know it, destined to change her whole life—for better or worse!

MAGIC OF LOVE

It was a far cry from London to Crags' Heights, the gloomy house in the Welsh mountains. But Barbara soon found herself forgetting the past in the face of the challenge presented by the aloof, mysterious Dominic Rockwood.

FACTS OF LOVE

At twenty-seven, Paula Grayson had been more or less forced into being a newspaper tycoon, but she was still a woman at heart, with all a woman's needs. And all her worldly success did not make up for the heartbreak of knowing that Gregory Scott had been using her to further his own interests ...

LOVE AND NO MARRIAGE

BY

ROBERTA LEIGH

MILLS & BOON LIMITED
15–16 BROOK'S MEWS
LONDON W1Y 1LF

CHAPTER ONE

SAMANTHA set her pen down beside her drawing board and slowly stood up. If she moved quietly and carefully she might be able to control her nausea until she reached the cloakroom. She walked to the door of her office and tried to turn the handle. Her hands were so damp that it slithered between her fingers. A quicker, more desperate attempt and the knob turned, allowing her to step out into the corridor. The cloakroom was only a few yards away, but the walk seemed never-ending. Her nausea grew worse and she clutched at her throat and tried to quicken her pace.

'Miss Gardner!'

Her secretary was calling her, but Samantha ignored it.

'Miss Gardner!' the voice called again. 'There's a call for you from the States. Shall I put it through to your office or ask them to ring back?'

A call from the States. Samantha forced herself to stop. She was expecting to hear from her New York office, and they would think it strange if she was not available. She opened her mouth to say she would only be a moment, but though her lips moved, no sound came out.

'Are you all right, Miss Gardner?' Her secretary was beside her, her freckled face anxious.

'I'm fine,' Samantha managed to croak out the words, then with a gulp she dashed for the cloakroom.

Fifteen minutes later she emerged, composed but pale. Her magnolia skin had lost its normal creamy tinge, and had a blue-white transparency that emphasised the fragility of her appearance. She was a small girl, an inch over five feet, with a brittle-boned look that gave no indication of her phenomenal energy and drive. Many people, seeing her

5

for the first time, took her to be a ballet dancer, for she had
the same lightness of movement. But a brief conversation
with her showed her to be a strong-willed business woman
who knew how to organise and control her own considerable talents.

Tottering back to her office, she collapsed on to the
leather settee normally reserved for visitors, and doubted
whether she would ever be able to control anything again.
With quiet desperation she wondered if the four years of
intense work she had done since leaving fashion school had
exhausted her to the point where recovery was impossible.

She imagined herself living in a cottage in the country,
miles away from people and noise, where all she need do
was eat and sleep. It was a life that beckoned with enticing
fingers, and she closed her eyes and succumbed to the
fantasy. She was only vaguely aware of her secretary flutter-
ing around, and of her assistant, Carol McLean, coming in
to look at her and then marching out again without uttering a word of sympathy.

I don't deserve sympathy, Samantha thought ruefully.
Doc warned me not to start work so soon. 'Flu always leaves
you feeling grotty.

She must have drifted off to sleep, for a brusque voice
jerked her awake, and she looked up to see Doctor Fergusson glowering at her.

'And what have you been doing to yourself?' he demanded, 'apart from everything I told you not to do?'

'That's what I've been doing,' Samantha quipped, her
husky voice huskier than usual. 'I was a bit under the
weather today,' she went on, 'but I'm fine now.'

'You look,' he said dourly, 'like a glass of skimmed milk
that's been standing too long.'

'It sounds delicious,' Samantha said.

'I'm not joking, girl. Lie still while I have a look at you.'

'There's nothing wrong with me,' Samantha protested.
'Carol shouldn't have called you. I suppose it was *her*?'

'It was,' the doctor replied. 'Now keep quiet.'

His examination was slow and thorough, which Samantha found surprising, since he had seen her in his surgery only two weeks ago. But he was acting as if he hadn't examined her for months, taking her blood pressure, listening to her heart, peering into her eyes and feeling her neck and throat with probing fingers.

'Well?' she asked, when he finally settled back in his chair, a portly, middle-aged man with alert eyes.

'Not at all well,' he replied. 'You should never have started work so soon.'

'But I felt fine, and I was at home for ten days.'

'It should have been twenty. Now it will have to be forty, maybe fifty.'

'That's impossible!'

'So is your continuing to work at this pace. If you don't want a complete collapse you must have a complete rest.'

'Oh, come on, Fergie,' Samantha chided, and stood up. 'I feel marvellous—look!' She held out her hands to show him how steady they were, and he caught one and prised her fingers apart.

'A complete rest,' he repeated. 'Even if your assistant hadn't called me, I was coming to see you today. I had the results of your tests, and want to talk to you about them.'

'Stop trying to frighten me,' Samantha said lightly. 'I know I've been overworking, but as soon as I've got this new American order completed, I'll take a long holiday. Did you know I've been asked to design a whole range for——'

'It will be the last range you ever design,' the doctor cut in bluntly, 'unless you sit down quietly and listen to me.'

'But——'

'Sit down and listen,' he repeated.

There was no twinkle in his eye, which was unusual for Dr Fergusson, and Samantha knew he was worried. She had only seen him like this once before: six years ago when he had told her that her mother did not have long to live.

'I know I've been pushing myself too hard,' she said. 'And I really will take a month off as soon as I can.'

'Make it three months, and make it now. You've been overdoing things ever since you left college, and your body is telling you it's had enough.'

'But I love my work,' she protested. 'I enjoy every minute of it.'

'You're wise to count your time in minutes,' he replied.

Blankly she looked at him. She did not feel desperately ill, yet Dr Fergusson would not talk to her like this unless he believed there was something seriously wrong.

'Your blood pressure is erratic and your heart rate fluctuates,' he went on. 'You have signs of an incipient ulcer and——'

'No more!' she cried. 'You've made your point. What do you want me to do?'

'I've just told you.'

'You can't expect me to leave the business for three months.'

'If you don't, you may be leaving it for ever.'

Samantha sat down on the settee. 'Is it as bad as that?'

'Yes.' The fact that he said no more emphasised the force of that one word.

'Very well, Fergie, I'll make arrangements to go away in a month's time.'

'Make it the end of the week.'

'I've a business to run,' she protested. 'I can't walk out and abandon it.'

'If you dropped dead, that's exactly what would happen.' He saw her eyes widen with fear, and give a slight shake of his head. 'No, no, I'm not saying you will. All I'm saying is that it might well happen if you don't take a complete rest. In a few months you should be fine.'

'And how long before I collapse again?' she demanded. 'I'm only twenty-five. If I fold up under a bit of strain at my age, how will I cope when I'm thirty?'

'By then, you may have learned some sense. You're an

intelligent young woman, Samantha, and a logical one. You should know by now that you can't burn the candle at both ends as well as in the middle.'

She knew this was true. Yet if she had not worked flat out she would never have achieved her success.

'Give me a few weeks to organise things, and I'll go,' she said.

'I'll give you till the end of the week. Any longer than that, and you'd better find yourself an undertaker, not a doctor.'

She chewed on her lower lip, then nodded. 'All right, Fergie, you win. Do I have to go to a nursing home?'

'Nothing like that. Merely dig a hole for yourself somewhere and disappear down it.' He eyed her thoughtfully. 'Do you have any friends with whom you could stay in the country? Not fashion friends,' he warned. 'I don't want you to even think of work.'

'Then that puts paid to my friends. I only have the ones I made in college.'

'Then stay in a country inn, or in some little seaside town as far away from London as possible. And don't tell anyone where you are. Make a vow to forget work completely. Imagine you're dead and that your company has to carry on without you.'

'I've often wondered if they could,' she said, with a quick smile that momentarily lit up her gamine features, 'and it looks as if I'm going to get the chance to find out.'

Dr Fergusson rose. 'Come and see me before you go. I want to give you a few prescriptions. And when you've decided where you'll be staying, I'll see if I know a good doctor in that area.'

'Do you think I might need one?' she asked, suddenly feeling vulnerable and not liking it.

'Not if you obey me and wind down completely. Become a vegetable, Samantha.'

'A big fat cabbage?' she smiled.

For the first time since he had come into the room, his

eyes twinkled, moving over her slightly built figure with its delicate curves and narrow bones. 'Never a big fat cabbage, my dear. More like a little Brussels sprout!'

Her smile at his remark died the moment he left the room, and Samantha sat at her desk and stared at her drawing board, longing to pick up her pen and start work again, but knowing she dared not. Dr Fergusson was right to warn her where she was heading. Yet how could she walk away from the business and pretend it did not exist?

'By telling yourself that it *doesn't* exist,' Carol McLean asserted when Samantha called her into the office and told her what the doctor had said. 'We've known for months that you've been heading for this.'

'I only had 'flu,' Samantha protested.

'You were ill long before that, but you wouldn't admit it.'

'I admit it now,' Samantha said ruefully. 'I feel dreadful. Shaky inside, and with a "don't-care" feeling.'

'We'll manage without you,' Carol said coolly. 'It won't be easy, but we'll cope. Luckily you've finished the new Collection and, if necessary, we can put it into production without you being here.'

'I'm only halfway through the American collection, though.'

Carol pulled at a strand of her hair. She was a big girl physically, in direct contrast to Samantha, whom she had met at college and for whom she had worked since they both graduated. In her own right she was a good designer too, but she lacked her friend's flair, which she privately thought was near to genuis. She was glad to be Samantha's second in command, seeing it as a duty to protect her from the day-to-day running of a business which had begun in a back room in London's West End and now took up the entire floor of the same building.

'Half a collection from you,' said Carol, 'is more than a whole collection from anyone else. If New York complains, I'll give them a flea in their ear!'

'I'll call Harvey Bender myself,' Samantha said. 'It's the least I can do.'

'Don't let him talk you into finishing the collection for him,' Carol warned. 'You know how persuasive he can be.'

'He can't be as persuasive as Dr Fergusson,' Samantha said drily.

'Have you thought where you're going?' Carol asked, taking the drawing board from Samantha's desk and placing it on the work table that stood by the large window.

'No. But it has to be somewhere where I'm not known and where I won't be encouraged to talk shop.'

Carol leaned on the table and folded her arms. 'I may have the solution. An aunt of mine has a gorgeous place in Cornwall. It overlooks the sea, and you can lie in your bedroom and hear the waves pounding on the rocks.'

'Would she want to bother with me?'

'She wouldn't be doing the bothering. She's on a world cruise at the moment. The last card I had from her was from Monte Carlo. But she left her housekeeper to take charge of things—a motherly old girl called Mrs Vivien— and she'll be delighted to look after you.'

'You think so?' Samantha asked doubtfully.

'I'm sure of it. As a matter of fact, leaving Mrs Vivien on her own was the one thing that bothered Aunt Meg. If you stayed there for three months and kept her company, it would be ideal.'

'If I went, you'd have to forget where I was. Doc told me not to let anyone know where I was going.'

'Once you're at Gable Cottage I'll forget you even exist,' Carol grinned. 'If you ring me to talk about the business, I'll tell you I never discuss my boss's affairs with anyone!' She moved to the door. 'I'll phone Mrs Vivien and tell her you'll be down at the end of the week.'

'Don't let her know who I am. Say I'm an out-of-work can-can dancer!'

Carol laughed. 'She can still know your name. I'll tell

her you're an artist if you like. That'll give you a chance to be eccentric!'

After Carol had gone, Samantha walked over to the window. It was the June solstice, and to herald the longest day of the year she had put on a buttercup-yellow dress, one of her own designs which she wore so well. Although she was slight, her work had a robust and vigorous style that had found her a world-wide market. She had begun by designing for the fashion-conscious nineteen-year-old, but within two years had also added collections for women in their twenties, thirties and forties, and six months ago had produced a fantastically successful collection for children.

Nothing succeeds like success. This was something she had always known, and her own success had proved it, for once she had reached the top of the fashion tree she had found other trees to climb. Now there was SAM jewellery, SAM fabrics, SAM make-up and even SAM food, guaranteed to keep women young for ever. The world was her oyster, although it seemed that the shell was threatening to close in upon her unless she rested for a while.

She frowned and pushed her short black hair away from her forehead. It was a wide, serene forehead, unlined above narrow, dark eyebrows and slanting, almond-shaped eyes. The eyes, with darker rims surrounding the grey irises, gave an exotic appearance to a face that would otherwise have been tomboyish, with its tiptilted nose and wide, mischievous-looking mouth. High cheekbones sloped down to a pointed chin which, allied to the shape of her eyes, gave her the look of a dainty Siamese cat.

She returned to her desk, suddenly weighed down by the thought of her beautiful house in Chelsea, her growing bank balance, the hundreds of people who depended upon her talent for their jobs and the thousands—nay—millions —of women all over the world whose style in dress she had influenced. No wonder she was on the verge of collapse! She had been driving herself for years without anyone giving her emotional support. Jonathan had been the last per-

son who had tried, but in the giving he had also b
demanding, and eventually his demands had outweighed
whatever he had offered.

'I love you,' he had said, 'but I can't share you with the
world. I want a wife, not a phenomenon.'

'My work is part of me,' she had tried to explain. 'In the
same way that your work is part of you.'

'But I don't live it night and day.'

He was a biochemist and a brilliant one, but able to
forget his work when he left the laboratory. Samantha's
peripatetic way of life had at first fascinated him and then
horrified him. But Samantha had loved him because they
were so different and had hoped they would complement
each other. But it had not worked out that way. Jonathan
wanted her to give up all she had achieved, to take the vast
amount of money she had earned and be thankful for it.
He had not realised that money was a secondary consideration and that Samantha's strongest need was to be creative.
She had found it difficult to believe he had not appreciated
this aspect of her character. But he hadn't, and small argu-
ments had become blazing rows which culminated in their
parting.

'I'll always love you,' he had said, but she had known he
loved the image of her, not the real woman. As she had
loved the image of the man she had wanted him to be.

She shifted restlessly. Why was she thinking of Jonathan
today when she had put him out of her mind for more than
a year? She no longer loved him nor did she have any re-
grets about parting from him, except perhaps for a feeling
of sadness that she would never find the type of man she
needed.

She wanted the impossible. A man who was strong
enough to dominate her; whose own work was sufficiently
important for him not to be jealous of hers, yet who was
gentle and kind. And that was why her wishes were fantasies, for a man who could understand a woman to that
degree was unlikely to have the strength of character to

make him a success in other fields, and she knew she would have to settle either for strength or tenderness, and cease hoping she would find both of them embodied in one person.

'It's all arranged.' Carol was back in the room, beaming. 'I told Mrs Vivien to expect you on Saturday. I wasn't sure if you'd be driving down, so I warned her to stay in all day.'

'I don't want a car there,' Samantha said quickly, 'or I might be tempted to get on the motorway and tear back here to see how things are going.'

'I've told her to lock the doors,' Carol joked. 'You've got to forget who you are until the middle of September. If you don't, there's no point in your going away.'

'I know, and I was only teasing. I'm going to totally forget Samantha Gardner. From Saturday onwards I'm an out-of-work painter.'

'That's better than a can-can dancer,' Carol grinned, and eyed her friend's yellow dress. 'But not too much out of work. Your clothes are obviously expensive SAM creations.'

'I'll only take old things down with me,' Samantha assured her, 'plus some paints and canvas. I really will paint while I'm there. I haven't done anything for years and I used to be quite good.'

'For heaven's sake don't start a second career!' Carol exclaimed with such horror that Samantha burst out laughing.

'I promise I won't do that. All I want is peace and quiet.'

It was a good thing Samantha could not see into the future, for peace and quiet were the two things she was not going to get at Gable Cottage.

CHAPTER TWO

THE hired car stopped at the corner of the lane and the driver pointed his hand towards the end of it.

'Gable Cottage is down there,' he explained. 'And if you carry on down *this* road you come to the sea. It's only a five-minute walk. Would you like me to take you there to have a look at the beach?'

'I would rather go to the cottage first,' Samantha told him, and perched expectantly on the edge of her seat as he turned the wheel and slowly drove down a narrow lane.

Tall hedgerows of honeysuckle blotted out the view on either side, but ahead of her she saw a rustic gate with the words 'Gable Cottage' written on it. The car stopped and the driver got out and reached for her case.

Samantha followed him, eager to see the house that was going to be her home for the next three months. Even as late as yesterday she had doubted whether she was doing the right thing to go to a place she did not know, and to stay with a woman who might object to taking care of a stranger. But Carol, who had spoken to Mrs Vivien on the telephone, had assured her the woman was delighted by the prospect of having someone to stay with her.

'She'll love looking after you,' Carol had insisted. 'I've told her you work for the same firm I do—which strictly speaking is quite true—so you won't need to worry about her guessing who you are. She says you're to bring nothing with you except clothes and books to read, and that in next to no time you'll be fat and well.'

'I can do without getting fat,' Samantha had chuckled and, because she had felt so much better in the last few days, had still wondered if she should delay her enforced rest. But a reluctance to incur her doctor's wrath had decided her against it and now, finding herself shaking like an aspen after a comparatively short journey, she realised how near the end of her tether she was.

Moving ahead of the taxi driver, she opened the gate and walked up the path. It was bordered on either side by flowers she had, always associated with the country: Sweet Williams, foxgloves, Canterbury bells, marigolds, pinks and huge clumps of lavender whose scent rivalled the honeysuckle she could still smell in the air. Beyond the flower beds lay the lawns, well tended yet still managing to look countrified. All the rose trees and a profusion of rose bushes seemed to grow up from the very grass itself, and clumps of lupins bordered the narrow beds that lay either side of the front door.

Carol had warned her that the cottage was not small, but even so it was larger than she had expected. But in every other way it was exactly as its name had made her picture it, with leaded windows and a beautifully-kept thatched roof that made her think of farmhouse teas and clotted cream. A rose-covered porch protected the entrance from the sun and, as she approached, the door was swung back by a plump, maternal-looking woman whose welcoming smile quickly dispelled Samantha's misgivings.

'Welcome to Gable Cottage,' Mrs Vivien beamed, and bustled forward, round as a cottage loaf in a dark dress and an enveloping white apron. Her hair was black but liberally sprinkled with grey and worn in two plaits coiled on either ear.

'I daresay you could do with a cup of tea. I've been keeping the kettle on the hob since two o'clock.' She turned her smiling gaze to the taxi driver and directed him to take the case into the hall.

Samantha paid him, but he seemed reluctant to leave, and she understood why when Mrs Vivien asked him if he would like to join them for a cup of tea.

'I wouldn't say "no" to one of your cakes either,' he grinned.

'I'm afraid you're out of luck, Bob. I meant to do some baking this morning, but I had a bit of a turn and had to lie down. But I've some nice biscuits.'

'Your second best is as good as first choice from anyone else,' the man chuckled, and followed the two women into the house.

The hall was rectangular in shape, with whitewashed walls criss-crossed with dark beams, and a beautiful red-tiled floor. The furniture was well-polished oak, gleaming with the same brightness as a large copper bowl filled with flowers, which stood on a narrow side table.

'The sitting-room is on your right,' the housekeeper explained, 'and the dining-room is on the left, as well as a little study which Mrs Barclay used when she was answering her letters.'

Samantha glanced briefly at the closed doors and then at the staircase facing them, which led up to the first and only floor.

'There are five bedrooms upstairs,' Mrs Vivien said. 'I'll show you round later.'

She led the way into the country-style kitchen. The floor was tiled here too, and the walls were painted a delicate apricot which went well with the pine fitments and the strings of onions which hung from a hook near the dresser. There was a pine table and chairs, and an extremely modern-looking electric stove and refrigerator. A fire glowed in a shiny black grate and a large kettle hissed merrily on the hob beside it.

'It beats me how you can have a fire in this heat,' said Bob.

'I probably won't light it now I have a visitor to look after,' the woman replied, 'but it kept me company when I was on my own.' She smiled at Samantha. 'I suppose you think that's a funny thing to say?'

'I can understand it. A coal fire is happy to look at.'

'Exactly.' Mrs Vivien poured boiling water into a large

brown pot and filled three cups with thick milk, golden as cream.

Sipping her tea, Samantha felt some of her shakiness ebb. She did not contribute to the conversation, content to leave the older couple to talk as she nibbled a biscuit. It was delicious and she had a swift image of home-made pies and succulent roasts. All in all it looked as if her decision to come to Cornwall had been a wise one, and she was suddenly sure that very soon she would be well enough to return to London and her work. But she must not think of that. She must completely forget the bustling factory and the hundreds of people whose jobs depended on her fertile imagination. Even to think of them made her start to shake again, reminding her that getting well was not going to be as quick or as easy as she would like to believe.

'Have another biscuit,' Mrs Vivien said. 'You're thin as a stick.'

'I'm not thin,' Samantha smiled. 'Just small-built.'

The woman sniffed and joggled the plate again, but Samantha shook her head and instead held up her cup to show she wouldn't refuse some more tea. The housekeeper reached for the pot and then gave an unexpected groan.

'What did you say?' Bob asked.

Mrs Vivien groaned again and Samantha, seeing something was wrong, moved quickly over and gently eased her back into the chair. The pink cheeks had turned sallow, but the woman tried to give Samantha a reassuring smile.

'I'll be ... fine in a ... in a minute,' she gasped. 'It's one of my turns. It'll soon give over.'

'Aggie said you hadn't been well lately,' Bob put in, and then, in an aside to Samantha, murmured that Aggie was his wife and a good friend of Mrs Vivien's. 'She said she told you to go to the doctor,' he went on, 'but that you were too obstinate to listen.'

'I can't abide doctors. Leave things to Nature, is my motto.'

Mrs Vivien tried to speak cheerfully, but her pallor

showed she was still in considerable pain, and though she enjoined Samantha and Bob to have more tea and not take any notice of her, they both found this impossible.

When ten minutes had passed and the woman had still not recovered, Samantha decided to take matters into her own hands and asked Bob the name of the local doctor and how to get hold of him.

'It's Dr Baxter,' Bob said. 'He does surgery from five to six-thirty every evening.'

'Then I suggest you take Mrs Vivien to see him now,' Samantha advised.

The housekeeper frowned, as if she did not like the idea, but Samantha gave her a reassuring smile.

'There's probably nothing seriously wrong with you, but it's a good idea to make sure.'

'What will you do? You've only just arrived and I can't go out and leave you.'

'I don't see why. I have my unpacking to do, and I expect you'll be back by the time I've finished.'

'I've stuffed a chicken for our supper,' Mrs Vivien said. 'It should go into the oven at six.'

'We'll think about food when you get home,' Samantha replied, and helped the housekeeper to her feet.

When the car finally drew away from the gate, Samantha breathed a sigh of relief. Despite her comforting remarks, she was not as sanguine about Mrs Vivien's condition as she had pretended.

As the noise of the engine faded into the distance and the silence of the countryside took over, she realised for the first time in a long period what it was like to be alone. In her factory and office she was constantly surrounded by people, and even when working on her designs was always aware of her staff near at hand. At home she usually had the company of her housekeeper, Mavis, and Mavis's husband who did odd jobs around the house. And then there were the constant phone calls from customers all over the world, with their demands, orders, wishes; every one of which had to be dealt with in record time, so that she rarely had a moment of quiet to think about herself.

It was no wonder that the constant pressure had drained her emotionally. Even making the decision to send Mrs Vivien to the doctor had left her trembling with exhaustion, as though she had been working non-stop for days. Dr Fergusson had been right to order her to the country. She needed peace and rest to rebuild her reserves.

Putting aside the thought of unpacking—the mere idea of it was enervating—she decided to explore the house. Next to the kitchen was a small dining-room, its french windows overlooking a lush green lawn. Beyond a neatly clipped hedge stretched a limitless panorama of ripening cornfields, and she stepped out and, for a few minutes, relaxed on a wooden chair that stood under a shady beech tree. Somehow the sun seemed far hotter here than in London. But then the rays did not need to penetrate through smog-filled air in order to reach one's skin.

With a contented sigh she returned to the kitchen and from there into the sitting-room. This was large and comfortably furnished with chintz-covered easy chairs and settees. There were flower pictures on the walls and the parquet floor was almost completely covered by a Persian carpet whose soft tones were picked out in the linen curtains that hung at the windows.

The study was furnished in a far more masculine way, and Samantha supposed it had once been used by Mrs Barclay's husband. A beautiful Queen Anne desk stood in front of a leather-backed wing chair, and she had to resist the urge to curl up in it and go to sleep.

Instead she collected her case from the hall and went up the narrow flight of steps to the next floor. There were five bedrooms here, three of them with their own bathroom and the other two sharing a bathroom between them. One of these two bedrooms was occupied by Mrs Vivien, as was evidenced by the photographs of old-fashioned-looking children and family groups that stood on the dressing-table beside a range of tortoiseshell trinket boxes. Of the three main bedrooms, the most luxurious belonged to Mrs Barclay, and Samantha peeped in quickly before going to the room next to it which, though more simply furnished, gave her a beautiful view of the fields.

She was about to start unpacking when something—she did not know what—prompted her to go into the bedroom on the other side of the staircase. It was smaller, but it looked out over the lane and, by standing at the farthest corner of the window, she was able to see the silvery blue shimmer of the sea. She gave a gasp of pleasure. She loved the sea. Its ever-changing colours, its restlessness and yet its eternal sameness had a soothing quality for her that could not be bettered.

Carrying in her case, she dumped it on the floor and then went to stand by the window again. How long would it take her to walk to the shore, she wondered, and would she need to scramble down any cliffs to get to the beach or could it be reached by the lane itself?

She had almost decided to set out and explore when the telephone rang.

'Dr Baxter's sending Mrs Vivien to hospital,' Bob told her. 'It's her gall-bladder and she must go in at once.'

'Will you be taking her?' Samantha asked.

'I'm on my way now. But we'll be stopping off to collect some of her night things. I thought if you could get them ready, we wouldn't have to hang about waiting.'

'I'll go right away,' Samantha promised. 'Does Mrs Vivien have any family that I should call?'

'None in this part of the country.'

'Then I'll go with her to the hospital. She won't feel so nervous if she isn't alone.'

'That's very thoughtful of you,' said Bob. 'We'll see you soon.'

Quickly Samantha went into the housekeeper's room and collected her night things, together with an additional nightdress which she found in a large chest of drawers.

Then she went into the bathroom to collect the woman's toiletries, as well as a pair of red fleecy slippers. She could not find a suitcase and, bundling all the things in her arms, she ran down to the kitchen and tipped them into a carrier bag. It was not the most elegant way to arrive at a hospital, but it was practical.

A hooter sounded and she grabbed the carrier and dashed down the garden path. Bob came forward to meet her and opened the front door of the car for her to get in beside him. Mrs Vivien was lying in the back, still pale but able to smile.

'I don't know what to say about this, miss,' she muttered. 'It couldn't be more awkward, what with you just arriving and me being taken off to hospital. If only it had happened last week.'

'It did happen last week,' Bob grunted before Samantha could speak. 'But you've got a bee in your bonnet about leaving the house unattended and——'

'Mrs Barclay doesn't like the cottage to be left. The antiques are very valuable and so are the paintings.'

'A person's life is more valuable still,' Bob muttered angrily. 'You should have had more sense.'

'It's all worked out for the best,' Mrs Vivien said stoutly. 'Fate sent Miss Rose along to help me.'

It took a second for Samantha to realise that she was the Rose in question. Then she remembered that Carol had suggested it would be easier for her to hide her identity if she pretended that her second Christian name was her surname.

'Having you here will make all the difference.' Mrs Vivien was still speaking.

'In what way?' she asked.

'Because the cottage won't be left unoccupied and I'll be able to stay in hospital with an easy mind.'

Bob's snort prevented Samantha from commenting. 'We aren't a village of thieves, you know!'

'It's the camping site further along the coast that I'm worried about,' Mrs Vivien muttered darkly. 'There are always people snooping around.' She fixed Samantha with a stern look. 'That's why I never leave the place for more than an hour at a time, and I'm careful to bolt all the doors and windows at night. But with you staying there, I'll feel much happier.'

'Which is more than Miss Rose will be,' Bob laughed 'now that you've practically frightened her to death with your silly talk of burglars.'

'As a matter of fact I wasn't thinking of remaining at the cottage,' Samantha intervened. 'I thought it would be better if I moved into a hotel.'

'Whatever for?' Mrs Vivien tried to sit up, but the movement pained her and she groaned and fell back. 'Please don't do that, miss. It's a lovely house to stay in, and with the good spell of weather we'll be having, you'll enjoy it.'

The idea of staying alone at Gable Cottage was something that had not occurred to Samantha, but thinking about it, it did not seem such a bad idea. She had come here for peace and quiet, and what could be more peaceful than a Cornish cottage miles from the nearest town?

'There's plenty of food in the larder,' Mrs Vivien assured her. 'I haven't used half the fruit I bottled last year, and if you don't want to do much cooking you can always get fresh eggs from the farm, and Bob here supplies me with all the vegetables I need from his own allotment.'

'You won't be lonely either,' Bob added. 'My wife will be happy to call on you and so will half the village, unless you make it clear you don't want to be bothered with them.'

'I didn't realise country villages were so friendly,' Samantha smiled.

'They're not. They're just nosy and they'll want to see you for themselves!'

Samantha laughed outright. 'You mean after the first rush I can expect no more?'

'Depends if they take to you.'

'Who wouldn't take to a little thing like you?' Mrs
Vivien said. 'If you——'

Her words died away in another gasp of pain, and
Samantha was relieved when Bob started to drive faster.

Within twenty minutes they arrived in Penzance. Dr
Baxter had telephoned to say his patient was arriving, and
a porter with a wheelchair was waiting for her in the foyer.

'If you would like to come to the ward with your
mother . . .' the porter said to Samantha.

'She's a friend,' Mrs Vivien interposed.

'But I would like to come up and see you settled,'
Samantha said, and followed the housekeeper into the lift.
They got out at the third floor, and a nurse led them to an
empty bed at the far end of the ward.

As the nurse helped Mrs Vivien to undress behind the
flimsy cotton curtains which surrounded the bed, Samantha
thought about her decision to remain alone at Gable Cottage. It would probably do her good to fend for herself. If
Mrs Vivien had been there, she would soon have become
bored doing nothing all day. Now she would have to keep
the cottage clean, as well as shop and prepare meals. She
might even enjoy playing house for a while.

But not for long. That was the trouble. Her womanly
urges would always be in conflict with her career. Surely
there existed a man who would accept the two sides of her
character and not want to change her the moment he put a
ring on her finger? They weren't all like Jonathan.

Even as she thought this, she remembered several boy-
friends who had been more than willing to let her go on
working. Yet perversely, this in itself had turned her
against them, for she had seen their admiration as a love of
her success. Maybe she wanted the impossible: a man who
would appreciate and encourage her ambitions, yet love her
for herself and not for her talents.

The nurse drew back the curtains, and Samantha saw
Mrs Vivien lying in bed with a thermometer in her mouth.

Samantha walked towards the bed, smiling reassuringly.

'The doctor will be in to see you shortly,' the nurse explained, taking out the thermometer and looking at it. 'Are you a relation?' she asked Samantha.

'A friend of the family,' Samantha replied, deciding that if she gave herself some importance in the nurse's eyes, the medical staff would be more willing to tell her about Mrs Vivien's condition. 'You'd better leave the patient now,' the nurse went on. 'Visitors' hours are between three and four in the afternoon and between six-thirty and eight in the evening.'

'Don't bother visiting me,' Mrs Vivien said quickly. 'Just as long as I know your at the house, I'll be satisfied.'

'I'll pop in from time to time,' Samantha replied. 'And I'll be phoning the hospital to find out the latest news.'

'There's no need for you to put yourself out by staying at Gable Cottage,' Bob remarked bluntly as they drove away from the hospital. 'Mrs Vivien takes her responsibilities far too seriously.'

'I think that's why Mrs Barclay likes her so much,' Samantha felt it necessary to say. 'Anyway, it makes no difference to me. I was intending to stay for three months anyway.'

'Been ill, haven't you?'

Samantha hid a smile. She had wondered how soon Bob would start asking personal questions.

'I've been working too hard,' she explained. 'Then I had 'flu and couldn't shake it off.'

'You work in the same firm as Miss Carol, don't you? She's a great girl. I've known her since she was a kid.'

'She's my closest friend,' Samantha told him, and knew she had said the right thing, for Bob's smile became warmer.

'If you feel like a gossip at any time, you can always drop in and see Aggie. There's a slate with a lot of telephone numbers in your kitchen. You can ring any of them, and you'll find someone to talk to you.'

Samantha remembered this when she found herself back in the kitchen half an hour later. Dusk was already softening the sharp outlines of the trees and giving a blue tinge to the kitchen, which she immediately dispelled by switching on the light.

The larder was even fuller than she had hoped. There seemed to be hundreds of jars of bottled fruit and jam on the shelves, and the refrigerator was well stocked with eggs, butter and several delicious-looking cheeses. But before she prepared supper she would have a bath.

The plumbing was as efficient as the rest of the cottage had led her to believe, and she gave a sigh of relief as boiling water flowed into the tub. Gable Cottage might be miles from civilisation, but it had all the mod. cons. The water was unbelievably soft and one quick rub of the soap produced a fantastic lather, thick and white as snow. After soaking for about twenty minutes, she clambered out, wrapped herself in a thick white towel and padded into her bedroom to collapse on the soft quilt.

Slowly her skin cooled and dried, and fighting off sleepiness, she swung her feet to the ground and stood up. In the nude she was like a Dresden figurine, with her fine bones and delicate curves, her skin as translucent as the best porcelain. Her breasts were small but beautifully shaped, with firm, rosy nipples. The line of her hips was long and gave her body the grace of a gazelle, as did the slender legs with their shapely calves and high insteps. Samantha could have been a ballet dancer or a gymnast if she had not preferred fashion design.

She slipped on the housecoat which Carol had given her as a present before she left London. It was more feminine than the clothes she usually wore, but she had to admit that the pink silk suited her, as did the flowing Grecian style.

Downstairs in the kitchen she hesitated. She was hungry but did not relish the prospect of cooking. Besides, it was a long while since she had done any. With Mavis to look after her, she rarely made herself anything except an occasional cup of coffee.

'It'll do you good to get back to basics, my girl.' She spoke aloud, her voice sounding surprisingly strong in the quiet of the room. Instead of making her feel less lonely it had the opposite effect, emphasising the emptiness of the house and its isolated position.

Quickly she glanced through the window. It was completely dark outside; not the friendly darkness of London, which was always broken by street lamps and the headlights of vehicles, but an impenetrable black void. Even the room was obliterated by the haze that covered the sky, and the earth seemed as if it were shrouded in black velvet, with Gable Cottage the only sparkle of light upon it.

Hurriedly she filled an electric kettle and plugged it in. Embers still glowed in the grate, but she had no intention of building up the fire. There was a limit to her desire for the rustic life. While the kettle boiled, she wandered into the larder and found a packet of cornflakes and a jar of bottled peaches. Putting some cornflakes into a soup plate, she swamped them with the fruit before sprinkling them lavishly with brown sugar.

Enthusiastically she began to eat, enjoying this meal far more than the Cordon Bleu offerings with which Mavis had tried to tempt her flagging appetite in the past exhausting weeks. Already London seemed a million miles away, as did the problems of coping with factory output and workers, of buying materials and making sure that clothes were ready on time.

Samantha pushed aside her empty plate, then spooned more sugar into her tea. She must find a shop that sold decent coffee—that was one thing she did not intend to forgo. She yawned and stretched, then almost jumped out of her skin as the clock chimed. It was a large, old-fashioned one which stood on the mantelpiece above the hearth and told her that the hour was nine. Only nine. She yawned again. She felt as if she had not slept for weeks. But perhaps her extreme tiredness was a sign that she was unwinding. She yawned again. Three months of unwinding lay ahead of her and the first day of it was barely over.

Deciding to leave the dirty dishes in the sink until the morning, she tottered wearily up to the bedroom. Her foot was on the top stair when the telephone rang and she hurried down to answer it. It was a nurse from the hospital, asking her to bring a dressing-gown and another nightdress when she next came to see Mrs Vivien.

'I brought all I could find,' Samantha explained.

'Mrs Vivien said you should look in the airing cupboard.'

'Fine. I'll bring them tomorrow.'

'Make it the day after,' the nurse replied. 'She'll be having her operation in the morning.'

'Operation?' Samantha echoed. 'I hadn't realised she was as ill as that.'

'She'll be fine once the operation is over. Gallstones are very painful.'

Samantha put down the receiver, more shaken by the news than she cared to admit. Although she had accepted the fact that Mrs Vivien might have to stay in hospital for a week or two, she had half hoped that Dr Baxter was too pessimistic, and that the housekeeper would be home in a matter of days. Now it looked as if she really would be on her own for some time, and the prospect was no longer pleasant. Of course she might feel differently tomorrow when the sun was shining, but at present she felt distinctly apprehensive.

In an effort to banish her nervousness, Samantha went in search of the linen cupboard which, as she had expected, stood between two of the bathrooms and also housed the hot water tank. A pile of Mrs Vivien's clothes lay on a shelf, including several nightdresses and a bulky looking camel dressing-gown. It seemed for too thick for the summer but, since there was no other dressing-gown in sight, she carried it with the rest of the housekeeper's night things into her own bedroom and put them on a chair.

She had still not unpacked all of her own things, and decided to do it in the morning. The pills she had taken before supper were already beginning to have their effect. They were vitamins and sedatives, so Dr Fergusson had informed her, and she had dutifully promised to take them regularly.

Pulling aside the eiderdown, she slid between the sheets. They were smooth as glass and smelt faintly of lavender. She pulled the eiderdown around her and snuggled against the soft pillow. She was going to enjoy being here. She would visit Aggie in the morning and ask her if she knew of a teenage girl who would come in the evenings to cook and keep her company. If she could find one, then staying here would be no hardship. Her lids closed and the long silky lashes lay like dark crescents upon her cheeks. For an instant the lids fluttered, and then were still.

CHAPTER THREE

A LOUD, persistent banging dragged Samantha back to consciousness. Groggily she sat up and reached for the bedside lamp. The noise was coming from downstairs. Someone was banging at the front door. Quickly she glanced at the bedroom window, almost as if she expected to see a face, then chided herself for being foolish. The caller, unless he had wings, had no means of getting up to her bedroom.

The knocking started again, louder this time, and she peered at her wrist watch, surprised it was only midnight. She felt as if she had been asleep for hours. It must be those darned pills. Tottering to the wardrobe for her housecoat, she stopped and then reached for Mrs Vivien's camel-hair one; fear of a male intruder made her decide she would be safer wearing a garment that disguised her femininity rather than enhanced it.

Quietly she went downstairs, nearly tripping over the long dessing-gown. There was a momentary lull between the loud banging, and she called out in a clear but nervous voice: 'Who are you and what do you want?'

'I want to come in. My name's Jackson and you are expecting me.'

The voice was very definitely male, being deep and dark brown. It was funny the way she gave everything a colour or texture. Voices in particular always had colour for her. Johnnie's had been a straw-coloured one, and Dr Fergusson's was deep blue. But the voice on the other side of the door was sable brown with another underlying colour. Black perhaps. She shivered and with an effort spoke more firmly.

'It's too late for me to let anyone in. Please come back tomorrow.'

30

'And where do I spend the night?'

'In a hotel.'

'There's no hotel in this village and I'm damned if I'm going to drive to Penzance at this hour. For heaven's sake open the door! I'm not a thief, I'm a friend of Mrs Barclay's.'

Samantha caught hold of the banister rail. 'Mrs who?' she asked faintly.

'Mrs Barclay, damn it! Your employer. You are her housekeeper, aren't you?'

Samantha hesitated and the voice spoke again, still sable brown but with less black on it. 'Look here, I can understand you being nervous about letting me in, but I assure you I'm perfectly harmless and exactly who I say I am. My name's Jackson and I met Mrs Barclay when her cruise boat called at Monte Carlo. I told her I was looking for somewhere quiet to stay in England and she kindly suggested I should come here.'

'Here?' queried Samantha.

'Here,' the man re-echoed in a tone of growing impatience that immediately made Samantha tinge his voice with red instead of black. Even without seeing him she guessed he was a bad-tempered old curmudgeon. 'I need somewhere quiet to get on with my work—which I can't do in my own home in Monte Carlo in the summer. Too many friends are always dropping in.'

Samantha did not reply, uncertain what she should do. After a short silence the man banged impatiently on the door again.

'Look here, Miss ... er ... I really do assure you I'm very much *persona grata* with your employer. If it were not such an ungodly hour I would suggest you telephone her on the boat. She's crossing the Mediterranean towards Suez by now.'

'I'll call her in the morning,' Samantha said quickly.

'And what do I do in the meantime—make myself a willow cabin at your gate?'

'I don't see you as Viola,' retorted Samantha, pleased at her quickness in following his Shakespearean allusion. But the man ignored her answer.

'Do be a sensible woman and open the door,' he said. 'What do I have to do to convince you I'm a friend of Mrs Barclay?'

'I don't know,' Samantha replied, feeling slightly foolish, for the man's story rang true. 'How did you meet her?'

'Through mutual friends. We share the same lawyer, actually—Howard Cramb. You could try calling him, though he won't take kindly to being disturbed at this hour.'

Still Samantha hesitated.

'Do you have a chain on the door?' the man suddenly demanded.

'A chain?' Samantha's fear returned. 'Why do you want to know?'

'Because if you have, then put it on and take a look at me. If I strike you as a dangerous criminal then I'll doss down under the tree until morning, when you can ring Howard Cramb to check my credentials.'

Samantha found herself in a state of dither. Usually she was decisive in a tricky situation, but then she had never before found herself in a cottage miles from anywhere, with an obviously irate man pounding to get in.

'Well,' he demanded, 'are you going to open up?'

Samantha looked at the heavy metal chain which was already in position, and knew she was stupid to be afraid. With a chain holding the door, the man could hardly force an entry, and she might as well see what he looked like. Carefully she turned the lock, wriggled the chain to make sure it was firmly in position, and then cautiously opened the door.

She saw nothing except blackness and for one horror-stricken moment wondered if the man had made her concentrate on the front door so that he could sneak round the back.

'W-where are you?' she stammered.

'In front of you,' the man's voice boomed out of the darkness. 'If you have a porch light, switch it on.'

Samantha did so, recoiling as she saw the largest man she had ever encountered. He was not only tall but also immensely broad-shouldered, with long arms and powerful-looking hands, one of which her eyes followed as he raised it to his face.

Tilting her head, she followed the movement and saw he was considerably younger than she had imagined, probably in his early thirties. There were lines around his mouth and eyes, but they came from laughter, not age. In the electric light it was impossible to see the colour of his eyes, but they were unusually large eyes for a man, and set beneath thick, beautifully curved black brows. His nose was beaky and his hair thick and shaggy which, together with his deeply tanned skin, gave him the air of a pirate.

'Well?' he asked grinning.

'You don't look like a murderer,' she stammered. 'But I'm still not sure I should let you in.'

'Take this,' he replied brusquely, and through the aperture thrust something at her. She jumped back as if it were a gun, and he gave a sharp laugh. 'My God, you really are scared, aren't you?'

'You can't blame me. I'm not used to strange men demanding to be let in at this hour of the night.'

'It's only twelve o'clock.'

'That's very late in the country,' she retorted. 'I was fast asleep.'

'It would have been earlier if my car hadn't broken down,' he replied apologetically.

'Why didn't you telephone and warn me?' she asked.

'Because Mrs Barclay forgot to give me her telephone number, and she's ex-directory.' He paused. 'Well, go on—take it.'

Samantha looked at his hand and saw he was offering her a passport. Gingerly she took it. In the hall light she

saw it was a British one, and the photograph inside re-
sembled the man who stood on the doorstep. He was born
thirty-five years ago in May, under the sign of Taurus,
the bull, which seemed singularly appropriate. His profession was given as 'Writer', although the name, Bartholomew
Jackson, meant nothing to her. However, the passport did
confirm that he was a resident of Monte Carlo.

'Well?' he asked in a mild voice. 'Are you satisfied now?'

Cautiously she approached the door again. Bartholomew
Jackson was leaning on the trelliswork, an incongruously
masculine presence among the sweet scent of roses.

'It's so pleasant out here,' he went on, 'that I'm almost
inclined to stop arguing with you and sleep under the stars.'

'There weren't any stars earlier.'

'Well, there are now.'

His head tilted upwards, revealing a pugnacious-looking
chin and a mouth that was a total surprise: large, but as
well-shaped as a woman's, with curly corners, as if he often
smiled. If Mrs Barclay had invited him to come here—and
Samantha believed his story now—it must be most irritat-
ing to have had such a cool reception.

She closed the door to remove the chain, then opened it
wide to let him in. He was carrying a large, extremely
heavy-looking pigskin suitcase, but he handled it as if it
was the lightest polystyrene. She wondered what sort of
writer he was. A sports journalist perhaps. At close range
he was even more formidable-looking than he had been
outside. Conscious that he was staring at her, she regretted
her ugly camel-hair dressing-gown and dishevelled hair.

'I'm sorry I had to get you out of bed,' he said. 'If you
could show me to my room. . . .'

'I don't know which. . . .'

Abruptly the man gave an exclamation and bent down to
the mat by the front door.

'No wonder you didn't expect me,' he grunted, and
handed her a telegram.

She tore open the yellow envelope and read the enclosed

message. ARRIVING THIS EVENING STOP. GUEST OF MRS BARCLAY STOP. IF HER LETTER NOT ARRIVED CONTACT HOWARD CRAMB LONDON.

'I suppose I was out when the telegram arrived,' she said, feeling foolish. 'I never thought of looking at the floor when I came back.'

She led the way up the stairs and Bartholomew Jackson followed. At the door of a vacant bedroom overlooking the sea, Samantha stopped.

'Will this do?' she asked.

'Perfectly. I assume the bed's made up?'

'I don't know.'

He grunted and pulled back the counterpane. There were pillows and blankets and an eiderdown on the bed, but no sheets or pillowcases.

Still feeling groggy because of the sleeping pills, Samantha tottered towards the linen cupboard, then returned with arms full of bedclothes which she dropped on the bed.

'Don't bother to make it up,' he said sarcastically. 'I'll do it myself.'

'I was going to let you.' Samantha went to the door. 'I'll see you in the morning, Mr Jackson.'

Back in her own room, she slid thankfully into bed. It was comforting to know she was not alone in the house, even though she was sharing it with a stranger. Turning her face into the pillow, she promptly fell asleep.

Sunshine, bright as London sun never was, shone full on Samantha's eyes and woke her up. Instantly she was fully alert. When they had shared a room during their student days, Carol had always complained bitterly about people who were full of beans in the morning. But Samantha considered her early morning cheerfulness to be one of her nicest characteristics, and a great asset if she ever shared her life with a man.

The thought of a man reminded her of the one who was

sleeping not more than ten yards away. At least she supposed he was still sleeping; unless he was one of those hearty individuals who ran a mile before breakfast. It was only six-thirty and she lay back on the pillows again and pondered on the day ahead. She would spend the morning pottering around the house and garden and would then go into the village to make the acquaintance of some of the locals.

It was the thought of the villagers that made Samantha realise she was in an embarrassing situation. A young woman living alone in a house with a strange man would not excite any curiosity in a city, and even in most villages today it would only cause momentary comment. But not in this particular village, where Mrs Barclay was regarded as a pillar of respectability, and would not allow her home to be occupied by a comely young female and a virile man.

Yet short of one or other of them leaving, this was exactly what they would have to do. A smile tugged at Samantha's mouth. Mr Jackson was not her ideal choice for a companion—he seemed too abrasive for that—but at least he was a presence and, as such, would lessen her fear of being alone.

They should get on quite well, she decided, as long as they kept out of each other's way. They could have their evening meals together, so long as he did not expect her to cook for him, for she had the feeling that he could be fussy about his food. He seemed used to giving orders, too, and she was curious to know more about him. Was he a free-lance writer or a roving reporter for a newspaper or magazine? And did he make Monte Carlo his base between assignments in order to save British income tax. If that were the case, he must be very highly paid.

Relegating Mr Jackson to the back of her mind, she got out of bed, unpacked her case, then showered and slipped into jeans and a tee-shirt. Momentarily she regretted bringing only her oldest clothes with her, but she had deliberately refused to bring anything that would remind her of fashion.

'If I have no smart clothes, I won't think of work,' she had stated.

'Care to bet on it?' Carol had teased.

'I'm betting my life on it,' Samantha had replied solemnly, for Dr Fergusson's warning had made a deep impression on her.

Her tiredness last night had convinced her he was right, but this morning she felt fit as a flea and eager to jump around the house and start doing things.

Whistling tunelessly, she went into the kitchen and started to prepare breakfast. She would have fresh fruit and a glass of milk. The milk here was so good she would be quite happy to live on nothing else for weeks. Munching an apple, she carried a full glass to the window-seat and curled up on it, looking a bit like a sprite with her black flyaway hair and almond-shaped eyes, their grey colour clear as spring water.

A noise in the hall made her turn, and she saw Bartholomew Jackson come in. He too was casually dressed, but with an elegance more suitable for the Côte d'Azur than a Cornish village. His slacks were navy and of the finest linen, his shirt of the palest blue, which made his skin look like teak. Again Samantha thought what a powerful-looking man he was, and very attractive if one liked the huge virile type, which personally she didn't. She glanced at his massive shoulders, then his hands, which were surprisingly well-shaped.

'Good morning,' she said clearly. 'I hope you slept well.'

'Like a log.' He glanced around. 'I wasn't sure if I was expected to breakfast in here or in the dining-room.'

'You can have breakfast where you like. I don't mind. You won't be in my way.'

'Thanks.' His tone was dry. 'I'll have it in here. I haven't eaten in a kitchen for years. It upsets Arthur.'

'Arthur?' she asked hollowly.

'My manservant. My boss, I call him. He rules me with a rod of iron.'

Samantha stared at him and he smiled. A smile made a great deal of difference to his face and gave him a disarming charm.

'Coffee and toast will be fine,' he said, sitting down at the table. 'With marmalade, if you have any.'

'I beg your pardon?'

'I'm glad you do,' he said, 'because you're beginning to make me feel I should be begging *your* pardon.' His good humour was fast disappearing. 'You don't object to my wanting breakfast, do you? After all, you are the housekeeper, and Mrs Barclay assured me there would be no problem in my staying here.'

'There's no problem at all in that, but....' Samantha was about to tell him she was a guest here too, when he stood up irritably.

'Damn it all, I didn't object to making my own bed in the middle of the night, but I don't expect to have to make my own breakfast as well. Or do you feel it's your job to look after Mrs Barclay and no one else?'

'At the moment I'm not looking after *anyone*,' Samantha said, hiding a smile. 'I'm on holiday.'

'I see. Well, I'm sorry to have disturbed your holiday, Miss ... I'm afraid I don't know your name. Mrs Barclay only referred to you as Gladys.'

Samantha almost choked on the milk she was drinking but pretended she had a cough.

'Nobody calls me Gladys,' she said in a muffled tone.

'Your employer did.'

'Never to my face,' Samantha said firmly, not quite sure why she was not telling this man the truth, but mischievously deciding to keep him in the dark for a little longer.

'What should I call you, then?' he said testily.

'You look as if you could think of a few names without any help from me.'

He gave an involuntary smile, though it quickly turned into a scowl as she sauntered over to the sink and rinsed her glass before setting it on the draining board.

'There's no coffee, I'm afraid,' she said laconically. 'Will tea be all right?'

'It will have to be, won't it?'

He remained seated and she tried to remember where the bread bin was, then went into the larder and came out with a wholemeal loaf and a slab of butter in an earthenware dish. She put it on the table, together with a knife and plate.

'Marmalade?' he enquired crisply.

'I couldn't find any.'

He pushed back his chair and strode into the larder, emerging after a moment with a large unopened jar which he deftly unscrewed. The marmalade in it looked delicious and Samantha's taste buds stirred.

'I think I'll have some too,' she said, and looked at him with wide, innocent eyes. 'Would you object if I sat at the same table with you, sir?'

He shrugged and deftly cut several slices of bread. 'Do you object to looking after people?' he asked abruptly.

'Of course not.'

'Then maybe you're one of those females who are naturally bad-tempered in the morning.'

'I am never bad-tempered in the morning!' she said indignantly.

'You mean you're always like this?'

She swallowed hard. 'I'm on holiday, Mr Jackson. In normal circumstances I work extremely hard, and I enjoy it.'

'Really?'

He looked as if he doubted this last remark, and watched in silence as she made the tea and brought the pot to the table, then took a large jug of milk from the refrigerator and set it in front of him.

'It isn't good to take so much milk out of the refrigerator,' he commented. 'It goes sour very quickly.'

'In the South of France maybe. Not here.' Samantha poured herself another glass of milk. 'I could live on this,' she commented.

'You give the impression that's what you intend to do while Mrs Barclay is away.'

Samantha remembered to look indignant. 'I don't have to cook if I don't wish.'

'I'm here as your employer's guest,' he reminded her, and liberally buttered some wholemeal bread before spreading a generous portion of marmalade.

Samantha helped herself to a slice and did the same. It tasted delicious and she regretted that Mrs Vivien was not here to make some more. She glanced at her watch and wondered if the housekeeper was already in the operating theatre.

'You look as if you're enjoying that.'

With a start, Samantha returned her attention to the man opposite her, and saw he was looking at the marmalade.

'I am,' she said. 'It's the best I've ever tasted.'

'It's home-made,' he said, studying the jar.

'Not by me,' she quipped and, too late, tried to take back the words, for he gave her a peculiar look. 'I don't do much cooking,' she explained. 'Mrs Barclay eats very sparingly.'

'Not when she stayed with me,' he retorted. 'She gave every sign of thoroughly enjoying her food.'

'Because she was on holiday. But when she's here she— she's quite happy with omelettes and toast.'

'Are you trying to tell me you don't cook?'

'That's right. I'm a rotten cook.'

'What stops you from learning?'

Samantha almost said 'time', but again something prompted her to keep up the pretence. 'I—Mrs Barclay really engaged me as a companion rather than as a housekeeper.'

'She told me you were an excellent cook.'

'You know how it is,' Samantha said airly. 'One woman's meat is another man's——'

'Marmalade?' he finished. 'You must tell me who did make this.'

'A woman in the village,' Samantha lied.

'Perhaps she'll give the recipe to Arthur.'

'Your manservant?'

'At least you remember that,' he said in an expressionless voice. 'You may be lazy, but there's nothing wrong with your memory.'

'I'm not lazy!' She jumped angrily to her feet. 'As I said before, I'm on holiday and I wasn't expecting anyone to stay here.'

'If that's an invitation for me to move into a hotel. . . .'

'You might be more comfortable there.'

'I'll be very comfortable here, once Arthur arrives,' he said. 'He's more than capable of taking care of me. In fact, that's why he's coming. You see, despite what you feared, I had no intention of being a burden on Mrs Barclay's housekeeper. All I wanted was to enjoy the peace and quiet of this lovely house, which is even nicer than I'd expected.'

'Well, if your manservant is coming,' Samantha said in relief, 'you're perfectly welcome to stay here.'

'Thank you *very* much.'

The sarcasm was too obvious to be ignored and she coloured. She would have to tell him the truth. It would be too awful if he wrote to Mrs Barclay and gave her the impression that her housekeeper had gone mad.

'There's something you should know, Mr Jackson,' she began. 'I'm not——'

'Don't bother apologising for your lack of hospitality,' he cut in. 'From the minute I arrived here you made it clear you wanted me to leave. But now I've explained that I won't be needing you to look after me, perhaps we can call a truce. Mrs Barclay is obviously delighted with you—though I'm damned if I can see why—and I don't want to do anything to spoil your relationship with her.'

'That's very magnanimous of you!'

'I think so too,' he agreed, and poured himself another cup of tea with a slow deliberation that infuriated her.

How self-righteous he was, sitting there tearing her character to bits! The fact that she deserved it was beside the point. He should at least be more charitable and give her the benefit of the doubt. Dash it all, he had arrived in the middle of the night, totally unexpectedly and had made no allowance for that fact.

'You obviously resent the job you're doing,' he said, breaking into her thoughts. 'You seem to regard service as something to be ashamed of. For my part I see nothing wrong with it. To a greater or lesser extent we all give a service and are dependent upon one another.'

'I'm not in the least resentful at having to give a service,' Samantha retorted.

'Then maybe you don't like being a housekeeper. Do you want to do something more glamorous?'

'How clever of you to guess,' she said instantly. 'I want to be a model.'

'You're too short and skinny,' he told her.

Anger swamped her. 'Are you always so frank?' she demanded.

'I haven't noticed you pulling any punches with *me*. After all, I am a guest here and you've gone to great lengths to show me I'm unwelcome. Still, I pride myself on being a judge of character,' he went on superciliously, 'and like many young woman of today, you feel the world owes you a living. Pehaps you're a university drop-out.' His glance raked her from head to toe. 'You have a well-educated voice, so I could be right.'

'Bang-on, in fact,' she said sarcastically.

He looked so pleased with himself that her desire to tell him the truth began to fade with astonishing speed.

'Obviously working for Mrs Barclay is your way of opting out completely,' he added. 'You can stagnate in a backwater and let the world pass you by.'

'Exactly,' she said, looking at him with innocent eyes. 'No responsibility and no commitment. That's my idea of life.'

'And a man to look after you, I suppose? Or is marriage not considered the "in" thing among your generation these days?'

'I'm twenty-five,' she said quietly.

'You don't look more than eighteen.'

'That's because I've let life pass me by,' she said sweetly. 'But perhaps you'll inspire me with some ambition while you're here.'

'It's not my business to change your life style,' he replied abruptly. 'I save my preaching for my books.'

He was halfway through the door when she spoke.

'What sort of books do you write?'

Blankly he looked at her, then one black eyebrow rose. 'Rumbustious novels where the hero rapes the heroine on page one!'

'You mean you begin with an anti-climax?'

His laugh was quick and unusually melodious, but then he had a melodious voice. This morning, if she had to give it a colour, she would have called it sherry-brown, rather like his eyes, except that they had little gold flecks in them.

'Do you write under your own name?' she asked.

'An inversion of it. Jackson Bart.'

She gasped, amazed by the pleasure she felt at meeting a man whose books she had admired for so many years. She read each of his novels as they came out, and had found herself coming more and more under his spell. He was never sentimental but set out human predicaments in a straightforward way. He offered no easy solutions, yet he did not preach a philosophy of hopelessness, as so many modern writers did. You might finish a Jackson Bart book deeply aware of the sadness of life, but you never felt it to be an insoluble tragedy.

'I had no idea who you were,' she murmured. 'If you'd told me last night. . . .'

'You mean you would have made my bed—or offered to share it?'

Fury engulfed her, but before she could find the words with which to annihilate him, he had sauntered out.

What an impossible man he was! The milk of human kindness that flowed from his pen seemed to have soured considerably in his personal life. Like an actor who could assume a role when he stepped on to the stage, this man adopted a different character when he wrote. Jackson Bart might be a warm-hearted, intelligent man, but Bartholomew Jackson was an opinionated, arrogant bore.

'I pride myself on being a judge of character,' he had said, and had immediately shown his poor judgment by assuming her to be an eighteen-year-old drop-out. Even worse, one who was languishing in a backwater until some man arrived to rescue her. Bart Jackson was typical of many modern men. They thought a woman should either be servile and clinging, or totally independent of any man.

Samantha knew she was not being fair. She had deliberately deceived Bartholomew Jackson about herself, and was reading things into his remarks which he had not actually said. Yet it was hard to be impartial when she thought of him, and she realised it was impossible for her to remain here with him. Yet if she left the cottage in the hands of a complete stranger, Mrs Vivien would be very distressed.

Moodily Samantha crossed the hall, then paused as she heard someone coming up the path. She opened the door and saw a small, thin man of indeterminate age. He had a sharp, pointed face with ferrety eyes and sparse light brown hair. He wore a dark suit with an extremely white shirt which looked even whiter against his sallow complexion.

'Good morning, miss,' he said in a decidedly Cockney accent. 'You're Mrs Barclay's housekeeper, I take it?' He held out his hand. 'I'm Arthur. Mr Jackson may have mentioned me.'

'He certainly did.'

'I've brought a few things with me,' the man said, glancing over his shoulder.

Samantha followed his gaze and saw there were two cars parked in the lane: a large, dark red Mercedes which she guessed belonged to Bartholomew Jackson, and a grey station wagon packed full of parcels and cartons.

'Do you want to bring all those into the house?' she asked.

'If you don't mind, miss. They're for Mr Jackson.'

He walked rapidly down the path and Samantha followed, full of curiosity. She was amazed when she saw the exact contents of the station wagon: tinned foods from Fortnum & Mason, numerous hams and bulky sausages with French and Italian labels, an elegant breakfast tray with legs—no doubt for breakfast in bed—and several pillows of different sizes, together with a typewriter, two dictating machines and a desk lamp.

'Mr Jackson likes his little comforts,' she commented.

'Don't we all?' Arthur agreed. 'And why not? There's so much in life we can't have.'

'Too true,' she said solemnly, and wondered what there was that Bartholomew Jackson could not have. Precious little, she thought.

'I'll leave the machines in the hall,' Arthur told her, 'but I'd like to take the food straight into the kitchen if I may.'

Obligingly Samantha led the way and watched bemused as Arthur sorted things out, putting some food in the refrigerator and a great deal in the larder.

'Did you think you were coming to the desert?' she asked light-heartedly. 'There are shops in Cornwall, you know.'

'It was Mr Jackson's orders, miss. He didn't want us to be a bother to the housekeeper. Mrs Barclay assured him there was no need for me to come too, but he insisted. And so did I,' he added, lowering his voice as if he were uttering a great confidence. 'When Mr Jackson is at home I like to make sure he has the best of everything. It makes up for the times when he doesn't.'

'Doesn't?' she questioned.

'Like when he's researching a story,' Arthur explained. 'I've known him go off for three months and come back looking like a victim of a concentration camp. He made himself quite ill getting material for that novel about the tramp. You may have read it.'

'I did,' she said, remembering how realistic the story was. And no wonder, if he had lived like a tramp in order to find out how his hero had felt.

'I'm always telling him he should write a novel about a tycoon,' Arthur went on. 'But he always says rich men are predictable.'

'So are male chauvinists,' Samantha sniffed.

'Beg your pardon, miss?'

'Forget it. I was being funny.'

Ferrety eyes surveyed her. 'You're much younger than I thought you'd be. From the way Mrs Barclay described you to me I expected an elderly lady.'

'You're younger than I expected too,' Samantha replied hastily. 'Mr Jackson gave you such a wonderful build-up, I thought you'd have gilded wings!'

'Mr Jackson is too kind about me,' Arthur replied primly. 'All I do is my duty.' He unbent sufficiently to smile. 'Though I have to admit that I regard it as a pleasure. Mr Jackson is a wonderful man.'

'I'm sure he is,' said Samantha, and turned to go out. The room spun violently and she clutched at the wall.

'You all right, miss?' Arthur came towards her, frowning as he saw the film of sweat on her forehead.

'Only a bit giddy,' she said faintly. 'I ... I often get like that if I move too fast. It's anaemia.'

'Why don't you go and lie down? If you tell me which is your room I'll bring you a cup of hot lemon tea. I'll put some honey in it too—I brought a jar with me.'

'That sounds delicious,' she said shakily. 'My room is the second door at the top of the landing. But you'd better get settled in first.'

'Thank you, miss. I'd appreciate it if you could tell me where I'll be sleeping.'

Samantha thought of the other servant's room next to Mrs Vivien's, then decided that when the housekeeper returned from hospital she would not want to share her bathroom with a man.

'You'd better take one of the guest bedrooms, Arthur,' she said. 'It has its own bathroom and you'll be quite self-contained there.'

Arthur nodded and Samantha groggily returned to her room and lay down on the unmade bed. It was ludicrous the way she kept getting these attacks of faintness and trembling.

'Have a complete rest, and in a few minutes you should be fine,' Dr Fergusson had assured her. 'Peace and quiet will soon put you on your feet again.'

Samantha giggled, and wondered what Fergie would say if he knew the dramas she had gone through in the last twenty-four hours. The fact that she was still alive and able to laugh at them showed she was in better shape than either of them had realised.

CHAPTER FOUR

A KNOCK at the door awakened Samantha from a deep sleep, and with the vague feeling that she was reliving a past experience, she sat up. It could not be another unexpected visitor arriving in the middle of the night? But no, the sunshine was streaming into her bedroom and a warm breeze fluttered half-heartedly through the open window. The knocking came again and she realised it was Arthur.

'Come in,' she called, and Arthur entered, carrying a tray on which reposed a covered entrée dish and several smaller ones.

'I popped up at eleven with a hot drink for you,' he said, 'but you were fast asleep and I thought it a pity to wake you.'

'I was still fast asleep just now,' Samantha confessed ruefully, 'and you really shouldn't have bothered to bring me my lunch. Mr Jackson won't like you waiting on me.'

'You leave Mr Jackson to me,' Arthur said cheerily. 'Always remember that his bark is worse than his bite.'

Samantha propped herself against the pillows and Arthur placed the tray across the bed. It was the same tray she had seen him bringing out from his car earlier that day. It had a ledge round it to prevent the dishes falling off, and a holdall fixed to one side which could be used to prop up a newspaper or a book. There was even a ledge to hold a pencil.

'Did Mr Jackson have this designed especially?' she asked.

'He made it himself. He's a dab hand at carpentry. It's his hobby, you might say.'

'I'd have thought he'd consider it a waste of time. He

said he likes to pay people to do things for him, so that he can concentrate on his writing.'

'He concentrates too much on that, if you ask me,' Arthur stated. 'That's why I was pleased when he took up carpentry. It doesn't do you good to work with your brain all the time. Sooner or later it affects your body and you crack up.'

Samantha nodded. She would have liked to tell Arthur the truth about herself, but knew that if she did, he would feel obliged to pass the information to his employer.

'Have your lunch before it gets cold,' he admonished. 'I don't know your taste in food, so I made you the same as I did for Mr Jackson. It's only a snack. When he's working he doesn't like anything heavy in the middle of the day.'

Arthur's idea of a snack was two beautifully grilled baby lamb chops nestling beside a fresh endive salad, delicately flavoured with lemon. There was also a frothy lemon mousse wobbling in a round crystal goblet.

Arthur hovered at the foot of the bed until Samantha began to eat and, after the first mouthful, she gave him an appreciative smile.

'This is superb! You're an excellent cook, Arthur.'

'Mr Jackson had me taught. He's an excellent cook himself and he sent me to his old school.'

Astonished, Samantha stopped eating. 'You don't mean Mr Jackson went to a cookery school?'

'That he did. Though he has servants most of the time, he's a great believer in self-sufficiency. "That way, Arthur," he says, "you don't need to depend on anybody. And if a man has a profession which he enjoys, what does he need with a wife?"'

'What indeed?' Samantha said drily.

'Not that he isn't fond of the ladies,' Arthur added with a smile. 'But he likes to keep them in their place.'

'In the bedroom and not in the kitchen.'

Arthur chortled and Samantha grinned at him. It was still difficult for her to guess his age. He would look the

same at forty and at sixty, but she judged him to be somewhere in the middle. He was a manservant of the old-
fashioned kind, and she was not surprised that Bartholomew Jackson valued him so highly.

'I'll pop in later and see if there's anything else you want,'
he said, going to the door.

'Please don't bother. I'll come down and sit in the
garden.'

'Do you have anyone else to help you in the house?'

She looked at him blankly, until she remembered she
was supposed to be the housekeeper.

'I don't think so,' she replied, then added hurriedly:
'At least I—no, not regular help.'

She thought it would just be her luck if a daily arrived
that very afternoon. Still, she would cross that bridge when
she came to it. She might even use it as a means to confess
her identity and put an end to this joke.

After she had finished her lunch, she made herself tidy
and went down to the garden. Now that she had begun to
unwind, she was finding it an effort to stay awake, and she
sank on to a comfortable reclining chair and was soon drift-
ing off to sleep again.

'You don't believe in overworking yourself, do you?'

An incisive voice brought Samantha back to full consciousness, and she saw Bartholomew Jackson watching her.
He had changed into brief white shorts and his torso was
bare, covered only by a thick sprinkling of hair down the
centre of his chest. It was golden brown in colour and quite
different from the unruly brown hair that covered his head.

'Are *you* dressed for work?' she asked.

'I'm dressed for a rest. I've been working all morning.'

One side of his mouth turned up sardonically. 'I hope
my typing didn't disturb your sleep?'

'I didn't hear it,' she said candidly. 'Once I got on my
bed I was dead to the world.'

'And now you're recovering from your rest?' he asked
sarcastically.

'I'm recovering from having been ill,' she informed him and, seeing his disbelief, felt obliged to explain. 'I had 'flu a few months ago and I didn't take enough time off to recuperate.' He looked even more sceptical and her voice quickened. 'I'm not lying, Mr Jackson. I've been ordered to rest completely for three months.'

'Is that why Mrs Barclay took a world cruise?'

Giving him full marks for intelligent guesswork, even though it was wrong, she nodded.

'I thought so,' he said with satisfaction. 'She didn't give me the impression of enjoying herself, and now I've seen her house I can understand why. Obviously she would have preferred to stay here in the summer and enjoy this beautiful garden. It would have been kinder if *you* had offered to go away until you were better, and had given her the chance to find another housekeeper.'

Infuriated by his bland assumption that she was selfish, she glared at him.

'Mrs Barclay didn't want to replace me. She thinks I'm——'

'A treasure,' he finished for her. 'Which I find totally incomprehensible.'

'We all have different standards,' Samantha said icily, 'and since I obviously don't match up to yours, it might be better if we kept out of each other's way.'

'I agree.' Calmly he sat down on a reclining chair next to hers. 'Since I'm a guest here....'

Unable to tolerate his rudeness, she swung her feet on to the grass and stood up. The sudden movement, coupled with the heat and her general weakness, sent the horizon reeling and she swayed and sank back on the chair. Her throat was dry as parchment and she tried to swallow in the hope that it would moisten her tongue.

'Lie still.' A firm hand came on to her shoulder and pressed her against the foam cushions.

After a few minutes the world steadied and she opened her eyes and gingerly lifted her head. Bartholomew Jackson was lying in his chair with his eyes closed. But as soon as she went to move, he sat up and gazed at her, his sherry-brown eyes enigmatic.

'You really are ill,' he said. 'I apologise for not having believed you.'

'I'm glad you didn't think I was putting on an act.'

'Even the best actress can't change colour to order, and you went a most unbecoming shade of grey.'

She put her hands to her face and he half-smiled.

'Don't worry. You've got your tea-rose glow back again. That's the second time today you almost fainted. Are you sure it's only the result of 'flu?'

'Who told you I nearly fainted this morning?' she asked.

'Arthur.' There was a glint in the brown eyes. 'Don't confide your girlish secrets in him, Miss Rose. He tells me everything.'

'I'll remember that.'

'You still haven't answered my question.' His gaze narrowed. 'Are you sure it's nothing more serious than the aftermath of 'flu?'

'Quite sure.'

'Wouldn't it be better for you to stay where someone can look after you?'

So he wants to get rid of me, she thought mutinously, and said as pathetically as she could : 'This is the only home I have. If you don't want me to stay here I can always go to a hostel.'

'Stop playing for sympathy,' he said sharply, showing himself to be not quite as gullible as she had hoped. 'You work for Mrs Barclay, and if she wants you to remain here, that's fine with me.'

'I can't understand why she didn't write and let Mrs— and let me know you were coming here,' Samantha ventured.

'She said she would, but you know how forgetful she is.'

'Yes, indeed.' Cautiously Samantha set her feet on the grass and stood up.

'You don't need to run away from me, Miss Rose.' His voice came from behind her and she half turned to look at him. 'Now I know you aren't just being indolent, I don't object to you so much.'

'You're too kind,' she said sarcastically. 'But I still object to *you*.'

'Because my arrival has upset the even tenor of your life? Don't forget this is Mrs Barclay's home, and I'm *her* guest, not yours. I don't even require you to wait on me.'

'Good,' she said evenly.

'And I would also remind you that I don't expect Arthur to wait upon *you*.'

Her face flamed. 'I didn't ask him to make lunch for me, nor did I ask him to bring it to my room.'

'I doubt if you'd need to ask a man to do anything for you,' he said, giving her a long leisurely look that took in her slight figure in its tight-fitting jeans and skimpy tee-shirt. 'Just one waif-like look from those slanting eyes and most men would run to do your bidding.'

Samantha was delighted by the compliment but infuriated that he had made it in this context, for she had not attempted to gain Arthur's attention.

'If you don't want Arthur to look after me, Mr Jackson, you'd better tell him yourself. If I did, he might be hurt.'

The only answer she received was a sardonic snort, and she stalked into the house and out through the hall to the front garden. There were no chairs here, but the grass was dry and she lay down on it and closed her eyes.

Within a few minutes the chink of china made her open them and she saw Arthur beaming down at her, a tray in his hand. She looked hungrily at the pot of tea and thick slice of home-made cake.

'Don't tell me you just whipped that up,' she said admiringly.

'It isn't as light as it usually is,' he apologised, 'but I'm not used to the oven yet.'

'You mustn't wait on me like this, Arthur,' she said,

tucking hungrily into the cake. 'Mr Jackson doesn't like it.'

'He asked me to bring you tea.'

'Did he really?' Mouth full of crumbs, she stared at him.

'Well, his exact words were: "She's sulking on the other side of the house, so go and sweeten her up with some of your cake." '

The slight warmth Samantha had felt towards Mrs Barclay's guest evaporated once again. No wonder he was still a bachelor! He might say it was from choice, but personally she could not imagine any girl in her right mind wanting to live with him on a permanent basis.

'Dinner will be at eight.' Arthur broke into her thoughts. 'Mr Jackson doesn't like to eat earlier than that, but if you're peckish. . . .'

'After this lovely cake? I'm not such a greedy pig as I look.'

'You don't look at all greedy, if I may say so, miss. More likely undernourished, if you want to know the truth.'

'The nicest things come in small packages,' a deep voice drawled, and Samantha wondered how long Bartholomew Jackson had been listening to their conversation.

'Eavesdropping, sir?' she enquired dulcetly.

'Passing through,' he replied calmly. 'You should learn not to be on the defensive, Miss Rose. It's wearing for all of us.'

'I'm not normally on the defensive.'

'Only with me, eh?' White teeth flashed. 'I can see I'll have to tread carefully or you might send a bad report of me to Mrs Barclay.'

'I can't see that worrying you.'

'You'd be surprised what worries me,' he grinned, and sauntered past her to the gate.

From the corner of her eye she watched him go to his car and climb in. Instantly she rose and went into the house. She had been meaning to call the hospital to find out how Mrs Vivien was, but had been afraid to do so while anyone was within earshot. She lifted the receiver, but dropped it guiltily as Bartholomew Jackson reappeared.

'Don't mind me,' he said quietly, and walked past her into the back garden.

'I was calling the butcher,' she shouted after him. 'He'll be wondering why I didn't go in today for my meat.'

'That reminds me,' the man swung round. 'Arthur asked me if there are any good shops in the village, and whether you have any favourites.'

'F-favourites?' she stammered.

'Ones who give the best service,' he replied, enunciating each word as if he were conversing with an idiot. 'I want to get the best and freshest food possible. Lobster, for instance. I daresay you know where we can go for that. I'm very partial to shellfish.'

'So am I,' she said, and then stopped as he looked at her expectantly. 'B-but I don't go to—to any special place. I just go where the mood takes me.'

'A typical woman,' he muttered. 'Does that apply to all your shopping?'

'Yes.'

'Well, perhaps you can tell me where you went last time you bought fruit.'

She racked her brains to see if she could remember the names of any of the shops she had passed in Penzance or in the village, but nothing came to mind and she shook her head.

'I—I'm afraid I can't. I have an awful memory.'

'So it seems.' The look he gave her was scathing. 'You astonish me by your inefficiency, Miss Rose, you really do.'

Tilting her head high, she turned on her heel and went into the kitchen.

Later that evening, when Bartholomew Jackson was having a shower, Samantha rang the hospital. The news about Mrs Vivien was good, and she felt relieved, though apprehensive at the thought of getting to the hospital tomorrow. She had deliberately not brought her car to Cornwall, knowing she might be tempted to take the occasional trip up the motorway to London, and she now regretted her lack of transport. She would either have to travel into Penzance on one of the local buses or ask Bob to take her in his taxi, an extravagance which Mr Nosy Parker Jackson would be quick to comment on.

Leaving this problem till the morrow, she changed into another pair of jeans and discarded the blue tee-shirt for a red one. It made her hair look black as midnight and her skin pale as a camellia. Considering that her father was a bank manager and her mother a schoolteacher, it was amazing how exotic she looked. Which only went to show that there was a skeleton in every family cupboard, she thought humorously, with a vague recollection of having heard of her maternal great grandfather's frequent visits to Madrid to watch the bullfights.

After dabbing a touch of scarlet lipstick on to her wide mouth, she went downstairs to see if she could help Arthur. The table in the dining-room had already been laid and there were several pots bubbling on top of the stove, sending forth a delicious aroma.

'You've laid two places in the dining-room,' she said abruptly, 'but I'm not eating with Mr Jackson. I'm eating in here with you.'

'I don't think that would be right, miss.'

'It's perfectly right. I'm the housekeeper here and——'

'You are a young lady, and that is the way I'm treating you.'

She was sure he would not have behaved this way with Mrs Vivien, and thought how unfair it was that youth and prettiness should give a woman such a great advantage.

'I'd be more comfortable eating in here,' she insisted, and went into the dining-room where she quickly removed the extra place-setting from the rosewood table. She was only just in time, for as she returned to the kitchen, she heard an upstairs door slam and then quick footsteps, surprisingly light for a man of Bartholomew Jackson's size.

'What made your employer choose Jackson Bart as his pseudonym?' she asked Arthur.

'He wanted something he would remember, and he said he'd be less likely to forget his own name!'

'Bart,' she murmured, and tried to think of calling him that to his face. It was brusque and uncompromising and suited him far better than Bartholomew.

Nimbly Arthur sidestepped her, carrying a tureen of soup to the dining-room, and Samantha took her place at the kitchen table and waited for him to return. She was not sure if Bart would make any comment to Arthur about her eating in the kitchen, or even if he was aware that a place had originally been laid for her opposite to him.

Her curiosity remained unsatisfied, for Arthur did not refer to his employer when he came back to the kitchen and served out two plates of soup.

'I understand you wanted to know the names of my favourite food shops,' she said as they started their second course—a delicate fish mousse served with sorrel sauce—'but I don't go to any shops in particular, just where the mood takes me.'

'Aren't you interested in cooking, then?'

'Not really,' she confessed. 'I—I'm more keen on other —things.'

'And so you should be at your age,' Arthur agreed. 'Young girls aren't meant to worry themselves about shopping and cooking, at least not until they're married. These days even married women often avoid domestic chores. Still, there's nothing in the Bible that says a woman has to stay at home and cook while the man goes to work. If a couple want it the other way round, then good luck to them.'

He collected their plates, then went to the refrigerator and took out an ice-cream bombe.

'Mr Jackson has a very sweet tooth,' he told her, wiping away the film of moisture from the glass dish on which the ice-cream lay. 'I'll serve him first if you don't mind. I don't want to take it to the dining-room after it's already been cut.'

'Of course not,' she agreed, and watched as he carried the dish away.

Half the ice-cream was gone when he returned, which bore out his remark that his employer had a sweet tooth. Still, Bart was a giant of a man and would need quite a bit of feeding. It was a good thing he had brought Arthur down with him. Samantha shuddered to think what would have happened if he had expected her to do the cooking. But then, if she had, the charade would quickly have ended, and one or other of them might have felt obliged to leave, so as not to shock the locals. But with Arthur as a chaperone she could stay here as long as she liked. The only question was how long she could endure Bart Jackson's insolence. If he continued to annoy her, she would not be able to relax and regain her strength, and since this was the sole reason she was here, she would be defeating her object.

'Mr Jackson asked if you would care to join him for coffee,' said Arthur, heating the percolator.

Samantha was surprised by the invitation and hoped she was not going to be hectored again. But Bart Jackson's smile as she went into the dining-room was unusually pleasant, and though she saw a surprised look on his face as he noticed her jeans and tee-shirt, he made no comment on them.

Samantha poured the coffee and handed him a cup. He was dressed with an elegance that astonished her. He could have been dining at the Ritz instead of a Cornish cottage. His narrow-cut trousers were of black suede and emphasised his long, lean legs and flat stomach. His jacket, in the same material, was magnificently tailored, and sat smoothly across his broad shoulders. His recent shower was evidenced by the damp gleam of his hair, which curled over his forehead, giving him a cherubic look that was ill matched with the dominant nose and sharply glittering eyes.

She realised he was a man of many contradictions and wondered which was the real Bartholomew Jackson; the man who stood elegantly by the mantelshelf holding a tiny coffee cup in one large hand, yet still looking as if he would be at home in a boxing ring, or the writer with a mind as delicately poised as a tightrope-walker.

'Why did you refuse to dine with me?' he asked abruptly.

'You don't dine with Arthur,' she replied, 'and I didn't expect you to dine with Mrs Barclay's housekeeper.'

'I wouldn't compare you with Arthur.'

'That's a very chauvinistic attitude!'

He looked puzzled. 'Just the opposite, I would have thought. I'm treating you like a woman.'

'But that's chauvinistic, isn't it? Women want to be treated equally, not differently.'

'Oh God,' he said with feeling. 'Don't tell me your one of those.'

'One of what?' she asked sweetly.

'A feminist.'

'What's wrong with being a feminist?'

'They're generally women who want the best of both worlds: a seat on a bus and equal rights!'

'You don't believe in equality?'

'I believe in people getting fair play for a fair day's work; and I'm against any discrimination because of a person's colour, religion or sex. Does that answer your question?'

'No. It contradicts your attitude to women.'

'I like female company,' he said, 'particularly at meals when I'm not working. It helps me to relax.'

'I don't seem to make you relax,' she said demurely. 'I irritate you.'

'You don't irritate me,' he retorted. 'I'll admit you're not my idea of a housekeeper, but then you're not my house-keeper and if you satisfy Mrs Barclay....'

'I must do,' she replied. 'You said she spoke highly of me.'

'So highly that I'm amazed,' he said bluntly. 'You obviously have qualities which I haven't yet discovered. Perhaps you'd care to tell me what they are?'

'I'm good-tempered, docile and have a sense of humour,' she replied in an earnest voice.

'But you don't like cooking—or you would know the names of the best provision merchants. You don't like housework—or you would have made up my bed even though I did arrive at midnight, and you must be physically frail if an attack of 'flu can knock you out the way it has.'

'What an excellent judge of character you are, Mr Jackson! I can see why you're such a successful novelist.'

'Now you're getting at me.' He smiled openly. 'But I do happen to think I'm a good judge of character, even though you obviously don't agree with my assessment of yours.'

Before she could reply, the telephone rang. Bart Jackson reached out a long arm and lifted the receiver from the small table nearby.

'Hello,' he said tersely, then smiled, almost as though the person to whom he was speaking could see him. 'Bruce, you old devil! Trust you to find out where I was.... No, of course I don't mind you knowing, but don't tell anyone else.... What's that? Yes, I've already begun work on the play, but it's too early to say how it's going. Pretty well, I think, but give me another week or so before coming down. I want to knock it into better shape before I show it to you.'

Samantha tried not to listen to the conversation, but she was too conscious of the man opposite to make that possible.

'That was Bruce Dorland,' he said, when he had put down the telephone. 'He's a film producer.'

'A brilliant one,' she agreed, and Bart Jackson's eyebrows rose. 'Even a country girl like me knows a little about the arts,' she added. 'I read an article about him in one of the Sunday papers. They said he made an international name for himself with his last picture.'

'Plus a fortune.'

'Are you interested in money too?'

As soon as she asked the question, Samantha realised it was not one which a housekeeper would pose. However, the man did not appear to object, and gave it serious consideration.

'If one equates money with success, then I suppose you can say I am interested in it. But if you asked me whether I would prefer a million in the bank or the Nobel prize for literature, then I would choose the prize.'

'Because you already have a million.'

He looked affronted. 'Even if I had nothing, my answer would still be the same.'

'I'm amazed,' she said, not very tactfully.

'Because you've already formed your opinion of me and you don't want to change it.'

It was an accurate observation, proving that in this instance he knew her better than she knew herself. Whatever this man said, she would disagree with it. It was a form of self-defence, though she was not sure exactly what it was she was defending.

'I think we rub each other up the wrong way, Mr Jackson.'

'That's a pity.' He reached for the coffee pot and refilled his cup. 'I intend staying here for the next few months and it won't be pleasant if you keep sniping at me.'

'You're the one who's been sniping,' she countered.

'Me?' His brows drew together about his beaky nose, as if he were assessing what she had said. 'I suppose I was irritated to find you were so young. From the way Mrs Barclay described you, I expected a comfortable old soul. Instead of which I was faced with an undernourished student who looked as if she were ready to join a protest march—against me!'

She hid a laugh. 'But I'm not a student.'

'Rebellion still burns in your breast, though.' He stared at her intently. 'A sparrow with an eagle's heart.'

'Not so much of a sparrow,' she retorted. 'What would you say if I told you I headed an exceptionally successful business; that I was a huge dollar earner; that I've been engaged twice but can't find a man sufficiently self-confident to accept my success without being resentful of it?'

'I'd say you were a first-class liar,' he replied equably.

'And you'd be right,' she said sadly, choking back her laughter as she stood up, murmured goodnight and went to the door.

'Goodnight, Miss Rose. Dream your fantasies. Who knows, one day they may come true.'

'I live in hope,' she said demurely, and went upstairs to her room, wondering what he would say if he knew the fantasies were already a reality.

CHAPTER FIVE

IN the next few days the residents of Gable Cottage settled into a fairly amicable routine. Bart was so preoccupied with his writing that he was not even aware when Samantha hired Bob's taxi for an afternoon and visited Mrs Vivien in the Penzance hospital.

Bart's work was going well and he made an effort to be pleasant to Samantha. All the same, she could not relax when he was around, and reluctantly admitted to herself that she was growing to like him more. This was largely because of the picture Arthur drew of his employer, showing him to be a kind man, so vulnerable to others that he had built a defence around himself. It was difficult to think of someone of Bart's physical stature being vulnerable, but she knew that size had nothing to do with it. She herself was a prime example of how little one should judge from physical appearance. No one looking at her slight figure would guess at the energy and drive it housed.

Since her arrival in Cornwall she had been unusually subdued, but by the end of ten days her natural vibrancy began to return, and with it her restlessness. Now was the most difficult time of her convalescence, and she doubted her ability to stick to the three months which she had imposed upon herself.

One morning, to stifle an unusually strong creative urge inside her, she started to clean the downstairs sitting-room. Half-way through, her heart started to pound so violently that she had to stop and rest, and it was unfortunate that Bartholomew Jackson chose that moment to walk in. His eyebrows rose as he saw her reclining on the settee, but instead of making a sarcastic remark he muttered that he had left some papers in the room and did not like anyone but Arthur to touch them.

'I haven't touched them,' she informed him.

'What did you do, then—dust around them?'

She ignored the jibe. 'I thought you were using the study as your workroom. I didn't realise you were taking over the entire house.'

'You're a fine one to talk,' he said, glaring at her stretched out on the sofa.

'I do try to keep out of your way,' she said resentfully, and rose to leave the room; only to be brought back by his querulous demand that she remove her feather-duster and chamois leather with which she had been polishing the windows.

'Cleaning windows isn't a woman's work, anyway,' he muttered crossly. 'Nor is it necessary for you to do anything around the house when Arthur is here.'

'He's your servant,' she reminded him, 'not mine.'

'I know. But I'd rather you took it easily until you're well again. Arthur is used to coping with a far bigger house than this.'

'It's a wonder he stays with you.'

'He has plenty of staff to help him in Monte Carlo,' came the gentle reply. 'I know you like to think of me as a hard taskmaster, but I assure you I'm not.'

'I don't think of you as anything, Mr Jackson,' she retorted, and marched from the room carrying the feather-duster as if it were a banner.

Ruffled by the contretemps, she decided to escape from the house for a while. Donning a bikini and jacket, she walked down the lane to the secluded beach. She sat on the rough, sandy shore and looked longingly at the sea. Never a good swimmer at the best of times, she was reluctant to test her puny strength in the rolling waves, and contented herself with a little paddling. It cooled her down but only whetted her appetite for a proper swim. When she next went to see Mrs Vivien she would spend the day at a hotel in Penzance and use the swimming pool.

The elderly housekeeper was making excellent progress and would be out of hospital in another week. But she would need to convalesce and was going to stay with a cousin in the North.

'I know it sounds peculiar to spend a holiday in a place like Manchester,' she had smilingly told Samantha, 'but when you live in a seaside village it makes a pleasant change to see buildings on the skyline.'

Samantha, who longed for buildings on the skyline too, knew exactly what she meant.

'I'm sorry you've been landed with another visitor, though,' the housekeeper had added, when Samantha told her of the arrival of Arthur and his employer. 'I hope to be back at the cottage by the end of July, but if you need me earlier, don't hesitate to drop me a line.'

Promising she would do so if necessary, and omitting to mention that she herself was pretending to be the housekeeper, Samantha said goodbye to Mrs Vivien. She had arranged to bring her some more clothes, so that she could travel direct from Penzance to Manchester without having to make a tiring journey to the cottage, and wondered with some amusement what Bart and Arthur would say were they to discover Mrs Vivien's existence.

She was enjoying the thought of their faces when she heard the sand crunch, and she looked round and saw Bartholomew Jackson towering above her. He wore a golden brown towelling robe which barely reached his knees, and there were espadrilles on his sinewed feet.

Nodding at her briefly, he took off his shoes and walked towards the sea. She had already seen him in shorts, but in brief swimming trunks there was little left to the imagination, and the artist in her admired his perfect physique. He was the type of man Michelangelo might have chosen as a model. As a young man Bart could well have posed for the sculpture of the boy David, for there was the same look about the face, the same rough beauty in the tousled hair, strong calves and rippling muscles.

'Come on in,' he called over his shoulder. 'It'll do you good.'

It was exactly the offer Samantha was waiting for and, without more ado, she plunged into the foam, gasping as the cold water splashed against her skin. The man beside her struck out towards the horizon, his strokes long and firm, his feet leaving a trail of white spume behind him.

Samantha followed but soon tired and, rolling over on to her back, floated on the waves. This was perfect. Not even the South of France could be more beautiful. Cool water lapped against her body and the sun's rays warmed her face, the heat and the coldness mingling deliciously together to give her a sense of perfect well-being. A white vaporous cloud floated across the sun and she took it as a signal to return to the beach. Only then did she realise with dismay how far she had floated from the shore. In a panic she turned over and desperately started to swim.

'Relax,' a quiet voice said beside her. 'Go on your back again and I'll tow you in.'

Greatly relieved, she gave Bart a smile and did as he ordered. He turned on to his back too, and with powerful strokes carried her across the blue-green sea.

'You can carry on swimming now,' he said suddenly, and let her go.

She turned over on her stomach again, full of panic until she saw that the beach was only ten yards away. After a dozen strokes she was able to stand up and wade out of the water.

'Did you think I'd towed you the wrong way?' He was walking beside her, taking one step to her two.

'I wasn't sure,' she admitted.

'That's about the nastiest thing you've ever said to me.'

He sound genuinely hurt and she lifted her hand towards him.

'I'm sorry, Mr Jackson, I really am. And thank you very much for rescuing me. I would probably have drowned if you hadn't been there.'

'If I hadn't been there, you wouldn't have gone into the water in the first place.'

She nodded, and they walked back to their towels in silence. Samantha sat down on hers and let the hot rays of the sun dry her. Bart did the same, though he made an attempt to smooth down his hair, which was forming tight curls on his forehead and the nape of his neck.

'Is there Greek blood in you?' she asked.

'Is that an inspired guess, or have you read the blurb on the back of one of my books?'

'If I read it, I've forgotten it,' she said, and waited for his answer.

When it didn't come, she screwed up her eyes and looked at him. He was lying back on his robe, his body so relaxed that she knew he had fallen asleep. He must be very tired, which wasn't surprising, because the last couple of nights he had been working till the small hours of the morning. At one point she had woken up and heard the clickety-clack of his typewriter in the distance, and Arthur had told her at breakfast that he had gone into the study and found his employer asleep at his desk.

She wondered why a man who was so successful should work himself so hard, and then thought of her own life. Success was like a rotating wheel: once you set it in motion and jumped on it, it was difficult to stop it long enough to jump off.

But Bartholomew Jackson's success was different from hers. He had no workforce dependent on his designs, no fashion deadlines to meet. He could write where and when he wished; one book a year or three.

Rounded chin cupped in her hands, Samantha rolled over on to her stomach and studied him intently. She held up her arm and compared it with his. It was like a flower stem beside a tree trunk. Feeling like a Lilliputian in the land of Brobdingnag, she raised herself slightly and examined his face.

Sleep had smoothed out some of the lines on it, but those around his eyes and mouth were still visible. Again she noticed the fine shape of his mouth and wondered what he was like when he set out to charm a woman. According to Arthur, he did this with ease, though he had never tried it with her. But then why should he bother with an insignificant girl who always wore a scruffy tee-shirt and jeans?

She thought longingly of the beautiful clothes hanging in her wardrobe in London, and wished she could dazzle him with some of them. That scarlet silk, for example, which made her look like a poppy. It would be fun to make him see her as a woman; to take that sarcastic gleam from his eyes and turn it into something more slumbrous. Nervous at where her thoughts were taking her, she sat up hastily and a soft shower of sand fell away from her body.

'You're tickling me,' said Bart in a lazy voice, his eyes still closed.

'It was the sand, not me,' she said, embarrassed that he thought otherwise.

'Same thing. You and the sand are alike. You both get under my skin.'

With a lithe movement he sat up too. It brought him close to her and he rubbed his hand lightly upon her arm. Before she knew what he was going to do, his head blotted out the sunlight and his mouth came down on hers. It lingered there with a soft persistence that quickened her pulses and made her aware that only the flimsiest of materials separated their bodies. Knowing that the slightest response from her could put her in a dangerous position, she put up her hand and pushed against his chest.

Instantly he drew back and stood up. 'Come on, little one. It's time you had your tea.'

Feeling pleasurably cared for, Samantha slipped on her jacket and padded after him. Their shadows lay across the sand: Bart's large and overpowering, her own so small that she had an image of a defenceless cave woman being dragged along by a massive, broad-shouldered man with hair hanging down to his waist.

She chuckled and he turned to look at her.

'Never ask a woman to tell you what she's laughing at,' he said drily, 'because she won't.'

'How right you are!'

He gave a rueful grin and caught hold of her hand, slowing his pace so that she could keep up with him.

'Do you know I don't even know your name,' he said. 'And I always like to be on first name terms with a woman when I've kissed her.'

'It's Samantha.'

'That's bigger than you are.'

She sniffed. 'I never expected you to say the obvious.'

'Sorry, I won't do it again. My name's a mouthful too, that's why I'm called Bart. And incidentally, I have Corsican blood in me, not Greek.'

'I thought I detected a Napoleonic streak.'

'Now you're the one who's being obvious!'

She laughed and he squeezed her hand.

'I like your laugh, Samantha. That's a great giveaway in a woman. I've known some very beautiful ones who've put me off completely when they laughed. There was one gorgeous blonde who sounded like a goat, and another who brayed like a donkey.'

'I bet you've known many gorgeous blondes.'

'And many gorgeous redheads and brunettes.'

'Have you never wanted to settle down?' she asked.

'Why opt for steak—even if it's the best fillet—when you can also enjoy baby lamb, suckling pork and delicious lobster?'

'What happens when your digestion gives out?'

'That question is definitely *verboten*,' he said firmly, and she knew she should say no more.

They reached the lane and saw the thatched roof of Gable Cottage ahead of them.

'This would be an ideal spot to live in if fine weather was guaranteed,' Bart said idly. 'It's almost as beautiful here as it is in Monte Carlo.'

'Where did you live before you went there?' Samantha asked.

'In London. I still spend three months of the year there. I would have stayed in London this time, if Mrs Barclay hadn't offered me the use of her house. When my friends migrate south I hare back to the metropolis.'

'How mean of you!' she protested.

'But I let them have the run of my place,' he laughed. 'That's why they still remain my friends.'

'Don't you mind other people using your things?'

'Things can be replaced,' he shrugged. 'It's only people who can't.'

It was a doctrine which many preached but few believed, and even fewer practised, though she was somehow sure that this man did.

They reached the cottage gate and he held it open for her.

'Will you have dinner with me tonight, Samantha, or must I join you and Arthur in the kitchen?'

Colour warmed her cheeks, but she pretended to be unaware of it. 'I'll lay a place for myself in the dining-room.'

'Good. I also expect you to call me Bart.'

She nodded, feeling inexplicably shy. After all, she had shared a cottage with this man for more than two weeks; she had seen him in a variety of moods and from Arthur she had learned a great deal about him. She suddenly felt guilty that he knew nothing about her, and almost blurted out her identity. But Arthur chose that moment to come to the front door and the opportunity was gone. 'I'll tell him tonight at dinner, she vowed. When he's had a glass or two of wine he's more likely to be amused by the pretence.

Bart had tea alone in the study, but not until she heard the clickety-clack of his typewriter did Samantha feel it was safe to dart upstairs to Mrs Vivien's bedroom, which she carefully kept locked.

She had let Arthur believe that Mrs Barclay stored some personal things in there. Quickly she put some of Mrs Vivien's clothes in a case and took it into her own room. She would take it into Penzance tomorrow.

Still hearing the noise of a typewriter, Samantha decided to telephone Bob and arrange to meet him the next day at the end of the lane.

For the first few days after Arthur's arrival, Samantha had been on tenterhooks lest anyone in the village said something that would make him realise Mrs Barclay's housekeeper was in hospital, and she had breathed a sigh of relief when he decided he did not like the facilities offered by the village general store and would go into Penzance for his shopping.

Her phone call made, Samantha returned to her bedroom and fumed again at the bareness of her wardrobe. Yet it was a good thing she did not have something glamorous to wear. To have put on a pretty dress might have given Bart the impression that she was trying to attract him, and nothing was further from her mind.

Dragging out a pleated grey skirt, the only one she had brought with her, she placed it on the bed, together with the smartest of her tops, a short-sleeved blouse in grey silk that exactly matched the colour of her eyes. The outfit might not make her look her best, but at least it revealed a pair of shapely legs.

It was upon her legs that Bart's eyes fastened as she entered the sitting-room at a quarter to eight.

'Until this afternoon on the beach I was afraid your feet might be webbed,' he said gravely.

Samantha laughed. 'I don't have much cause to wear dresses down here.'

'Did you wear them anywhere else, then?'

She bit her lip, then released it quickly before he could see.

'How long have you been here?' Bart asked curiously.

Samantha hesitated. She was not sure what Mrs Barclay had told him about her housekeeper and, pretending she hadn't heard the question, she wandered over to the window.

'I love this hour of the evening when the colours are fading and everything looks purple and lavender.'

'I like the morning best,' he replied. 'It's fresh and untried, and one always gets the feeling that one can begin again.'

'Do you think one ever can?'

'No.' It was said emphatically. 'One has to accept one's mistakes and go on from there; learning by them, not forgetting them.'

'You have a realistic philosophy,' she commented.

'What's yours?'

'A sherry.'

He laughed, seeing through the ploy, and poured her a sherry and a whisky for himself.

'I'm honoured that you're wearing a skirt instead of trousers,' he said, raising his glass in her direction. 'You could be a very attractive young woman.' His lower lip jutted forward as he surveyed her. 'In fact, you *are* attractive.'

He was looking at her with an intensity which made her feel he was seeing her for the first time, and his next words proved it.

'You've been so self-effacing these last few weeks, Samantha, that I tended not to see you.'

'That's the way you like it when you're working,' she reminded him.

'But I'm not working now. I've come to a full stop and

I need Bruce's reaction before I continue. So for the moment I am free.'

His eyes ranged over her, examining her feature by feature, limb by limb, and she remembered the first time they met, when he had stood at the front door and angrily told her he did not intend to build a willow cabin at her gate.

' "Two lips indifferent red",' she quoted.

'I won't accept the word "indifferent",' he protested. 'They're a tantalising colour—even without lipstick.'

'You're flirting with me,' she replied coolly.

'Do you mind?'

'I think I do. Flirting is such a waste of time.'

'So we go straight to bed, then?'

Her gasp of indignation made him chuckle. It turned up the sides of his mouth, and told her that once again he had baited her successfully.

'Do you always tease the women you know?' she asked angrily.

'You aren't one of my women. You're a little slip of a girl with woodland grey eyes and dancing dark hair.'

Samantha was so enchanted by the compliment that her annoyance vanished, though some slight irritation returned as he put a careless arm across her shoulders and gave her a hug.

'You're a good kid, Samantha. The only female I know who hasn't got on my nerves when I've been working.'

'I'm not a kid. You're only ten years older than I am.'

'But a hundred years older in experience. Living in this backwater of yours you know nothing of life, and certainly nothing of the sort of life I lead.'

'Drink, drugs and women?'

'No drugs,' he said flatly. 'But a fair amount of drink and a lot of women. Now finish your sherry, because I've seen Arthur hovering in the hall, and that means the soufflé is ready to be served.'

Feeling a bit like a soufflé herself—poised and expectant but knowing that at any moment she might become completely flat—Samantha followed Bart into the dining-room. It was the first evening meal they had taken together and she knew, with a sudden frightening knowledge, that she wanted it to be the first of many.

CHAPTER SIX

BART had a fund of light conversation and he regaled
Samantha with stories of the many famous people he had
met during the course of his rise to fame.

She wished she had taken more notice of the short
biography she had once read of him, but could only remember that he had travelled extensively and had not
started to write until he was twenty-eight. His first novel
had been a world-wide best-seller, as had every subsequent
book.

Yet he was totally lacking in conceit. He regarded writing as a job and had none of the 'I'm a genius' attitude she
had encountered in far less talented people. In Samantha's
sphere there were many dress designers who, once they
achieved a little success, became insufferable, and it was her
own pet fear that she might develop in the same way. Because of this she went to great lengths to retain the friends
she had met in her student days, knowing they were honest
enough with her to destroy any pretensions she might
display.

'Has success made it difficult for you to make friends?'
she asked Bart as they returned to the sitting-room for
coffee.

'I haven't made new ones for years—a defence mechanism, probably. I only feel at home with the people who
knew me when I was a nonentity.'

'I don't think you were ever that.'

Bart chuckled. It was a melodious sound and had a
magical quality for her. What was there about this man
that she found so attractive? It was not his charm, for he
had barely started to exercise it with her. Nor could it be
his striking good looks, for she had never been turned on

by the purely physical. No, her liking for Bart had far deeper roots, and came from the knowledge that in this man she had met her match.

It was an exhilarating thought. Bart was the first man for whom she had felt this way, and she wondered what it would be like to be his wife. She was indulging in a wild fantasy, of course, for she knew he had no intention of disrupting the smooth pattern of his life by tying himself to one woman, any more than she would enjoy being married to someone so dominant. She was too used to being the controller of her own destiny to submit to anyone else's command.

Yet it was interesting to speculate on the sort of girl who might eventually succeed in capturing him. She would have to be exceptionally clever—cunning really—and sufficiently in love with him to be the docile partner he would require.

'I suppose a lot of girls run after you?' she said aloud.

'Too many for comfort,' he agreed. 'But it isn't the girls who worry me—I can deal with them—it's the older women who are far more difficult to shake off.'

'I'm sure you manage.'

'Occasionally I have to be tough.' He eyed her. 'But you see me as tough, don't you?'

Samantha did not reply, nor did Bart seem to expect an answer, for he rose and poured himself a brandy, lifting the decanter towards her and then shrugging as she declined. In his chair once more, he stared at the glass in his hand.

'My parents were divorced when I was eight,' he mused, 'and for most of my childhood I was shunted back and forth between them. My father genuinely loved me, though he was always too busy to give me much of his time. But my mother saw me as a pawn; a means of getting more money out of my father to pay for her extravagant whims; and even more extravagant boy-friends. She died when I was eighteen and I was never more glad of anything in my life.'

'Glad?' Samantha's breath caught in her throat. 'You can't mean that!'

'I do. It meant I didn't have to go on making excuses for her; that I didn't have to fight the knowledge that I was hating her more and more for what she doing to my father.'

'But they were divorced.'

'He never stopped hoping she would come to her senses and return to him. She was a nymphomaniac,' he said bluntly.

'Then you should have pitied her, not hated her.'

'I did both. But because I loved my father, the hatred won. It was only when she died that my father began to find some peace. He even managed to marry again and make something of the rest of his life.'

'Is he still alive?'

'Very much so. He lives in California with my stepmother. He doesn't love her the way he loved my mother, but he's content.'

'I can understand why you're so wary of love,' she commented.

'I'm more than wary. I refuse to let it happen to me. No person of intelligence should allow themselves to want one person to the exclusion of all others.'

'Then you will never allow yourself to fall in love?'

His answer was slow in coming. 'Sometimes one can't stop it. It happens when you least expect it.'

'And then what?'

'Then you root it out and run like hell.'

Samantha found her pulses racing. There was a depth of feeling in Bart's voice that told her he was speaking from experience, but whether the emotion that coloured his voice came from a past or present affair, she did not know. But the scowl on his face warned her not to question him.

'Damn!'

His expletive startled her and she saw he was looking down at his shirt, which was gaping in the middle.

'You'd think a paragon like Arthur could sew on buttons,' he grumbled. 'Yet he's never been able to master the simple use of cotton and thread.'

'I'll sew it on for you.'

'You?'

'Why not?' she said laconically. 'Most women can sew.'

'Most women can cook and keep house,' he replied, 'but you're not very good at either.'

Her colour rose. 'Because I haven't done very much since you've been here, it doesn't——'

'Come off it,' he interrupted. 'You didn't even know which shops to recommend. Nor did you bother to tell Arthur about the marvellous herb garden here.'

She could not hide her startled expression and, as he saw it, his own became more mocking. 'You see? You're just not typical of the average female.'

'Since you seem to despise the average female, you should be delighted.'

She expected a humorous rejoinder, but instead his lids lowered, turning his eyes into golden-brown slits. She did not know what she had said to disturb his mood, but the ease between them vanished and she sensed his desire to be alone.

'When you take off your shirt, leave it outside your room,' she said, moving to the door. 'I happen to be quite proficient with a needle.'

'If you're as good at using it as you are at giving it, you should be fantastic,' he drawled.

'Would it surprise you if I told you that I was an excellent —dressmaker?'

His eyes opened wide and he was suddenly good-humoured again. 'Is that your pipe-dream, little Samantha? To be a world-famous couturier? When I was teasing you before, you said something about being a huge dollar earner.'

'That's because I——'

'Don't waste your time on daydreams when you have all

your life ahead of you. I'm sure you won't find it difficult to meet a man willing to take care of you.'

'Like a pet dog?'

'A pet cat, more likely,' he grinned.

With a toss of her head she opened the door.

'Must you go to bed so early?' he enquired.

'I thought you wanted to be alone.'

'I did. But the mood has passed. Stay and talk to me a bit longer.'

Although she wanted to stay, she was unwilling to pander to him; or more to the point, to her own desire to do as he wanted. Murmuring goodnight, she left him. She did not know what she had expected from this evening, but was aware of a vague disappointment that it had not ended the way she had hoped.

I wanted him to kiss me, she admitted, and tried to imagine what it would be like to have his mouth passionate on hers, instead of merely tender, the way it had been this afternoon. That he was a man of deep passion, she was sure; as she was also sure he could control it. If only she could control her own feelings so easily!

Angry at her weakness, she went into her bedroom. She heard the sound of footsteps on gravel and, going to the window, saw Bart walking towards the garden gate, open it and then stride in the direction of the shore. It was not an evening stroll, for his pace was too brisk for that. His shoulders were thrust back and his arms were swinging, giving her the impression that he was a man walking away from a situation he did not like.

'It's me,' she whispered to her reflection in the window pane. 'I'm beginning to get under his skin and he doesn't like it.'

The thought was exhilarating even though she warned herself not to be excited by it. She was sure Bart had resisted far more skilful and lovely women; ones who would stake everything in their determination to win him. Yet he was still free, and that, more than anything else, should be a warning to her.

She thought of her past boy-friends and marvelled at her contrariness. They had all set out to prove their dominance over her, but none had succeeded. Yet Bart, who was not even trying, could have her for the asking. It was madness. If she had any sense she would pack her things and run away. She should finish her holiday in Scotland or Florida or Tierra del Fuego; anywhere far away from Bart Jackson.

But she knew she would not do anything of the kind. She would stay here and pit her wits against his, hoping that in the end she would manage to inveigle herself into his life before he became aware of it. By which time he would— she hoped—be too emotionally involved with her to want to escape. Her wish might turn out to be a pipe-dream, but by golly, she was going to enjoy smoking it!

In the morning she managed to carry Mrs Vivien's case through the house and into the lane without Bart or Arthur seeing her. Bart was in the study typing, while Arthur was cooking something fragrant-smelling in the kitchen. Samantha returned to tell him she was going to Penzance and to ask if there was any shopping she could do for him.

'I went in yesterday and did a lot,' he said cheerily, with a shake of his head. 'Just go off and enjoy yourself. You still look peaky.'

'I feel fine.'

'Maybe you do, but Mr Jackson has given me strict instructions to fatten you up.'

'For Christmas?'

'Why not? You'd be a lovely present for him. Not merely decorative, like so many of his lady friends, but nourishing as well.' Arthur's foxy features were softened by a broad smile. 'He's really concerned over you. It's unusual for him to be that way over a woman. "My scraggy kitten", he calls you.'

Grinning, Samantha went out. She had heard a car in the

distance and was sure it was Bob's taxi waiting for her at the top of the lane, as arranged.

Within moments she was sitting beside the Cornishman, driving to Penzance.

'And how's our famous author getting on?' Bob asked. It was his standard greeting every time he met her and she tried to vary her answer.

'He's relaxing a bit more. He's finished the first draft of his play and is taking a breather.'

'It must be easy being a writer.' Bob changed gear as the incline of the road increased. 'You just sit on your behind all day and let the words come out!'

'What happens if the words don't come out?'

'Then you wouldn't be a writer,' Bob said bluntly. 'After all, it's each man to his trade. Take you, for example. Typing and shorthand must come easily to you, yet for me it would be the hardest thing in the world.'

'For me too,' said Samantha and, seeing Bob's look of surprise, could have kicked herself. 'I'm not a secretary,' she added hastily.

'I thought you worked with Miss Carol?'

'I do, but I'm more of a general dogsbody in the office.'

'Picking up pins and suchlike?' He changed gears. 'What's she like to work for?'

'Carol?'

'No, no, the woman Miss Carol works for. Mrs Vivien said she's a famous dress designer.'

'She's very nice,' Samantha said cautiously. 'You'd be in for a shock if you met her.'

'I doubt it. I know what these fashion women are like— dressed up to the nines and thin as beanpoles.'

'This one isn't like that. She's charming, clever and very easy to work for. I love her,' Samantha added for good measure, thinking she might as well complete the picture and become a complete narcissist.

'Does that mean you're anxious to get back?'

On the verge of saying yes, Samantha found herself hesitating. 'In one way I'm keen to return, yet in another.... Living here is so much nicer than living in a city.'

'Then why not stay?'

'Because one has commitments. It isn't easy to pull up one's roots.' She paused, cogitating. 'But I'm going to pull out soon, though. There's more to living than working like a maniac.'

Bob let the conversation drop and Samantha was glad of the opportunity to mull over what she had said. Was it her illness and tiredness that had made her outlook change? As a dress designer she had reached the peak of her profession. She was sought after by every major store in the Western world, but did she want to go on spending the rest of her life designing clothes, bed linen and wallpapers?

What would happen to her if she did not stop? She had been critical of Bart for wanting to live his life alone, yet if she did slacken her work, she would be doing the same. And at least Bart had an unhappy childhood as a reason for avoiding close relationships.

'How long will you be with Mrs Vivien?' Bob interrupted her thoughts. 'I have a few errands to do in town for the wife and I'll be able to drive you back. I won't charge you,' he added.

'That's very kind of you, but I'm not sure how long I'll be staying. I might treat myself to lunch in one of the hotels.'

'You'll find them pricey. It would be better if you went to a café. I'll give you the name of a good one.'

Touched by his concern, Samantha wrote down a name, wondering what excuse she could give him for not eating at the café he had suggested.

Mrs Vivien was delighted that Samantha had brought her clothes, for only an hour earlier the doctor had given her permission to leave the hospital as soon as she liked.

'Are you sure you can manage without me at the cottage?' she asked.

'Quite sure,' Samantha said. 'And don't come back until I contact you.'

'I'm not on a permanent holiday, miss. Mrs Barclay's still paying my wages.'

'But she lent the house to someone else,' Samantha reminded her, 'and he's brought his own manservant.'

The housekeeper relaxed and Samantha reiterated her assertion that she should not return until she was contacted.

'I won't want to stay away more than three weeks,' Mrs Vivien said when they finally parted, 'so if I don't hear from you by then, I'll be back.'

Samantha thought of this conversation as she wandered in the town centre later, looking at the shops. Yesterday she had planned to tell Bart who she was but, as always, some trifling remark of his had angered her and robbed her of her good intention. Last night it had been his bland assumption that she could not sew. Tonight it would probably be something else, and she knew that the longer she postponed telling him the truth the more difficult it would be to do so. What had begun as a joke was fast developing into a deliberate subterfuge. Frowning, she paused in front of a dress shop, noticing that half of the window display was devoted to her own designs. How startlingly different they were from the other clothes shown, their bold colours and clean lines making them so obviously SAM garments.

'So there's a touch of the frilly feminine in you after all,' an amused voice drawled, and the warm fingers that lightly touched her forearm and set her body tingling, told Samantha that Bart was standing beside her. She turned to look at him towering beside her, his mouth tilted up at the corners, his thick hair ruffled by the breeze.

'I didn't know you were coming to Penzance,' she said.

'Ditto,' he smiled. 'Why didn't you tell me? I'd have given you a lift.'

'You might have thought I was asking to be taken.'

'You aren't the sort of woman who would ever ask to be taken.'

His tone made it clear that his words had a double meaning, and warm colour suffused Samantha's skin.

'I'm glad you're a country girl,' he said softly. 'Otherwise you wouldn't have the ability to blush so charmingly.'

Quickly she stared at the window again and he followed her gaze.

'Are you planning to add to your wardrobe?' he asked.

'Yes,' she said, and the urge to make him see her as desirable was so strong that she could cheerfully have bought everything in sight.

'I like that blue dress,' he remarked.

She followed his pointing finger, dismayed to see he was referring to a frilly creation in the smaller of the two windows, the section that was not displaying her own dresses.

'I was thinking of the apricot linen,' she replied, directing his attention to a dress she had designed six months earlier and which had proved itself a winner in the mass market.

'I don't like it,' he said emphatically. 'The colour's harsh and it has no style. A woman in that would look as if she were wearing a sack.'

'It's been a fantastic success,' she retorted.

'How do you know?'

'I—I read somewhere that it's sold by the thousand.'

'Which only shows how stupid women are! Look at the thing. It would flatten a woman's breasts and completely hide her waist. I bet that dress was designed by an effeminate man who can't bear the sight of a woman's body.'

'It's a SAM dress,' Samantha said faintly, feeling she had to make some protest. 'She's world-famous—and a woman.'

'An Eton-cropped Lesbian, probably!'

'Don't be so bloody sexist!' Samantha retorted. 'For a man of intelligence you're the most prejudiced, narrow-minded——'

'Go in and buy the blue one,' he interrupted. 'I have some things to do and I'll pick you up here in half an hour.'

'I wasn't going back yet,' she replied, still furious.

'That's a pity. I was looking forward to taking a picnic lunch to the beach and spending the afternoon there.'

It was too good an invitation to refuse and Samantha immediately gave in. 'I'll see you here in half an hour, then.'

'Good.'

He strode away and, a few yards from her, turned. 'The blue,' he ordered.

'What if they don't have it in my size?'

'Then get something similar. You'll look beautiful in it, Samantha.' He paused and gave her a sharp smile. 'You're a *Sam* too. Is that why you defended the old bag?' Without waiting for a reply, Bart waved his hand and went on his way.

Samantha entered the shop, all her instincts telling her to ignore Bart's advice and buy one of her own dresses. Instead she asked if they had the blue frilled one in her size. Unfortunately they did, and she tried it on. She hated it as much on herself as she had on the model, but remembering Bart's orders, she bought it. She was half-way out when she turned back and crisply said she wanted to buy three SAM dresses and did not wish to try them on.

'You're lucky to get them,' the assistant said, popping them into a dress box. 'They sell like hot cakes and we managed to get an extra supply sent down from London yesterday.'

Delighted that her clothes were so popular in Penzance, Samantha blithely signed a cheque, and was still in high spirits as she got into the car beside Bart.

'Perhaps you'd prefer to have lunch at a hotel,' he said abruptly. 'It must be pretty dull for you stuck at the cottage all the time.'

'I haven't found it dull,' she said. 'I would much rather have a picnic on the beach.'

She did not add the words 'with you', but knew they were the only ones that mattered. Again she was dismayed

by the strength of her feelings for this man, knowing they
were not based on rhyme or reason.

Perhaps Bart was a symptom of her illness. Once she was
completely fit she would regain her usual common sense
and he would fade from her mind. But as she glanced at
his profile, the heavy thud of her heart told her that nothing
in the world would eradicate the deep impression he had
made on her.

'Did you get the blue dress?' he asked.

'Your word is my command.'

'Wear it for me tonight.'

'Am I having dinner in the dining-room again?'

'Don't be a fool.' He was brusque. 'You know you are.'

'I never take anything for granted with you,' she explained.

'Am I so difficult to understand, then?'

'Not at all. You're quite easy to know. And one thing I
know for sure is that to take you for granted is the best
way of making you do the opposite!'

'What an observant little thing you are,' he chuckled,
catching hold of her hand and squeezing it.

His grip was firm, but not so tight that it was uncom-
fortable, and she realised that he was aware of his strength
and was careful how he used it.

'I could crush you with one hand,' he said, his words
almost echoing her thoughts. 'Normally I can't abide little
women. They generally use their smallness to hide their
determination.'

'You're too intelligent to generalise like that.'

'Then let's say I'm making the comment out of experience.'

'If you don't like small women, what experience can you
have had with them?'

'Enough.'

The abruptness of his tone suddenly made her wonder
if his mother had been a petite woman, but she did not like
to ask him.

'Yes,' he said flatly, 'you're right. She was.'

Samantha turned her head swiftly and their eyes met. 'You knew what I was thinking?'

'I always know what you're thinking,' he said so loftily that her mood of tenderness for him was overtaken by an urge to kick him.

Oh, Bart Jackson, she thought. How much fun I'm getting pulling the wool over your eyes!

CHAPTER SEVEN

SAMANTHA looked at herself in the full-length mirror and saw that the frilly blue dress was a disaster.

She knew she was always hyper-critical when it came to fashion, and for this reason rarely wore clothes made by any designer other than herself. But this dress was especially wrong for her, though she could understand why Bart had chosen it. She was small and fine-boned which, to the masculine mind, was synonymous with frills and floating fabric—both of which this dress had in abundance. Additionally it was blue—a favourite male colour.

She grinned at her image. Bart, in his ignorance, did not realise that the elegant lines of her own dresses, which he had seen in the shop window and been so critical of, would do far more for her delicate curves than this one would. Still, it was an improvement on jeans and tank top, which was something to be said in its favour. Dabbing some scent behind her ears, she went downstairs.

It was only as she reached the bottom step that she heard two men talking in the sitting-room. She recognised Bart's deep voice but did not know the other one.

'Does Mr Jackson have a visitor?' she asked, going into the kitchen where Arthur was making a lemon dressing for the endive salad.

'Yes. It's Mr Dorland. He arrived an hour ago.'

'Bruce Dorland?' Samantha frowned. 'I didn't know he was coming. You'd better clear away my place in the dining-room. I won't be having dinner in there.'

'Yes, you will, miss. Mr Jackson expressly said so. In fact that's why he didn't tell you Mr Dorland was coming. He knew you'd get on your high horse.'

'I would not!'

'What are you doing now, then?'

'Getting off my high horse,' she admitted wryly, and went into the sitting-room.

She was instantly conscious of Bart, devastatingly handsome in a white silk sweater and black linen slacks. Their afternoon on the beach had deepened his tan, and it made his eyes glow more gold than brown. His hair was brushed sleek, but a few tendrils still curled on the nape of his neck and she longed to smooth them down.

'Come in, Samantha, and meet Bruce,' he said, seeing her by the door.

Samantha smiled at the film producer, thinking what a pity it was that she had not met him in another time and place, for no man could be expected to compete with Bart and win.

Seen on his own, Bruce Dorland would have gladdened the heart of any woman. Average in height, with blond hair and vivid blue eyes, he looked as if he should be in front of a camera rather than behind it. He was about the same age as Bart, but was more formally dressed in a grey suit, the wide shoulders and lightweight material proclaiming its Californian origin.

'Now I know why Bart wanted a country retreat,' he smiled shaking Samantha's hand and holding it a little longer than necessary. 'Why didn't you tell me you had company here, Bart?' he said, glancing across at him. 'I wouldn't have wasted time worrying if you were lonely.'

'I can see you worrying,' Bart grunted, crossing to Samantha with a glass of champagne.

'What are we celebrating?' she asked.

'Bruce doesn't touch hard liquor,' Bart said drily. 'He once read somewhere that successful producers only drink champagne.'

Quickly she looked at Bruce and saw he was smiling broadly.

'Women shouldn't drink hard liquor either,' Bruce murmured. 'It ages them.'

'Samantha's a milk and honey girl,' Bart replied, looking at her. 'Isn't that so?'

'I quite like a saucer of cream on occasion,' she replied.

Both men laughed and Samantha accepted her drink and sat down.

'I think you were talking shop when I came in,' she said. 'Please don't let me interrupt you.'

Bart gave her a sharp glance, as if uncertain whether or not she was being sarcastic. Satisfied that she wasn't, he started talking to Bruce.

'You timed your arrival very accurately. I only finished the script last night.'

'As a matter of fact I only came down to prod you. I'd no idea you would have anything for me to read. You finished it far more quickly than I expected.'

'I had no distractions here,' Bart replied.

'I wouldn't say that,' Bruce commented.

Samantha felt the colour come into her face and hoped she was sitting too far away for him to see it. If only she did not have such an unfortunate habit of blushing! Holding her glass, she wandered over to the french windows and stepped into the garden, moving quickly out of sight. Unfortunately she was not out of earshot and was able to hear Bart's reply.

'Sorry to disappoint you, Bruce, but Samantha's not my girl-friend. She's Mrs Barclay's housekeeper.'

'Pull the other one, Bart!'

'Why should I lie? I've never been bashful about my girl-friends.'

'That's true. And I must admit this one doesn't look your type.'

'She isn't.'

'She's *my* type, though,' Bruce added. 'I like the way her eyes slant up at the corners. She's a bit like a doll.'

'I'm too old for dolls,' Bart answered.

'Which brings me to Linda,' said Bruce. 'I suppose you know——'

Not waiting to hear any more, Samantha blindly pushed her way through some straggling bushes to the far side of the garden. Trembling, she leaned against the privet hedge. It served her right for eavesdropping. Tears filled her eyes and she blinked them away. She was darned if she was going to cry because Bart had said she was a doll and not a woman. It was as well she knew what he thought of her.

'Samantha!' Bart was calling her. 'We're going in to dinner.'

'I'm coming,' she called lightly and returned to the sitting-room, smiling with a brightness she did not feel and focusing her attention on Bruce.

During dinner the film producer exercised all his charm on her. He was curious to know about her and was far more persistent in his questioning than Bart had been.

'How long have you lived in the country?'

'Too long for me to remember,' she prevaricated.

'Don't you long to get back to town?'

'If I did, I wouldn't remain here.'

'Were you a housekeeper in London too?'

Afraid that if she said yes he would ask for whom, she shook her head.

'What did you do, then?' he probed.

'This and that.' She saw his eyes crinkle and said: 'Let me keep a little bit of my mystery.'

'So long as you don't object to my trying to solve it?'

She laughed and batted her lashes at him, thinking that a girl who wore a frilly dress like this was expected to flirt.

'Something in your eye, Samantha?' Bart asked matter-of-factly.

She gave him an innocent look. 'What makes you think so?'

'The way you're blinking. I've got some eyewash upstairs,' he added unromantically.

'That will dislodge my false eyelashes,' she said sweetly.

'They don't look false to me,' Bruce put in gallantly.

'They're not.' Samantha gave him a bewitching smile.

'You came here to talk about the script, Bruce,' Bart broke into the silence that followed. 'Or have you forgotten?'

'Only temporarily, old chap.'

With an effort Bruce took his eyes away from Samantha and began to talk about the play which, Samantha learned from the conversation, he had read before dinner.

'It's bloody good,' Bruce stated. 'It reads as if you've been writing screen plays all your life.'

'I've enjoyed doing it,' Bart admitted.

'Then perhaps I can persuade you to write an original film script for me?'

'My stories always work out better if I write them as a novel first.'

'You can name any price you like. Would a hundred thousand and two per cent of the gross satisfy you?'

'Possibly.' Bart was astonishingly cool. 'But I doubt if it would satsify Cummings.'

'Your damned agent,' Bruce muttered. 'I can't decide whether he takes orders from you or you take them from him.'

'That's good.' White teeth flashed as Bart's tanned face creased into a smile. 'As long as we can keep sharks like you guessing!'

Bruce heaved his shoulders in exasperation and looked at Samantha. 'Our host isn't as hard as he sounds. The truth is he only gets Cummings to act for him because he'd be a push-over if he made financial deals for himself.'

'Don't expect Samantha to believe that,' Bart warned. 'She's already decided I'm as tough as old boots, and it will confuse her to think anything else.'

Bruce's eyes twinkled, but he returned to the subject after dinner, when he was alone with Samantha while Bart was making a telephone call.

'Bart *is* a push-over,' he said. 'But I'm sure you've already found that out.'

'Why should I have? I'm only the housekeeper here, whatever you may think to the contrary.'

'Some housekeeper!'

Lightly he ran a finger across her bare shoulder. Her frilled bodice was low-cut, and though her breasts were hidden by the dress, the violet shadow between them was visible. His gaze rested on it, then moved up to her mouth, a vivid cupid's bow in her glowing skin.

'You're wasted down here, Samantha. Have you ever thought of taking up acting?'

'I'm acting now,' she cooed at him.

For an instant he looked blank, then he gave a shout of laughter.

'You have a sharp little wit, haven't you?'

'It comes naturally to me, sir.'

'Do you ever get up to London? I'd like to see you if you do.'

'I'll call you and let you know.'

'I'd even come down here for a weekend if you promised to see me—alone, that is.'

His hand was on her shoulder again, and the shiver she gave was not one of pleasure, though Bruce did not guess it.

'Care for a brandy?'

Bart's voice made Samantha jump, though Bruce turned casually, as if he did not mind being seen making advances to Samantha.

'A brandy suits me fine,' he said. 'It's the only spirit to which I succumb.' He looked at Samantha again. 'Apart from a spirited woman.'

She laughed and, glancing at Bart, was surprised to see him scowling. Triumph quivered through her, but she quelled it. It was foolish to think he was jealous; he was merely being a dog in the manger.

'Linda's coming down tomorrow,' said Bruce as he accepted his brandy. 'She would have come with me today, but she had two retakes to do on her last picture.'

'I hope you told her there's no room for her here?' Bart replied.

'I'll leave you to do that. I know she's expecting you to put her up.'

'I'll feel safer if she sleeps elsewhere. You'd better make sure they have a room for her at the inn.'

Bruce laughed and winked at Samantha. 'Our Linda's a man-eater—and she's particularly hungry for Bart.' He looked at his host. 'At one time I thought you felt the same?'

'I did. But I lost my appetite for her when she started hearing ringing in her ears.' His mouth curved sardonically. 'Wedding bells!'

'Then how come you suggested I offered her the role of Diana?'

'Because she's ideal for it.'

'Linda sees it as a sign of your returning affection. If it isn't, you'd better convince her otherwise.' Bruce's blue eyes rested on the small, curvaceous figure sitting beside him. 'You could always pretend Samantha was your new girl-friend.'

'No, thanks,' Samantha said instantly. 'I'm a terrible actress. I could never pretend to like Bart sufficiently for that.'

'Not even if you made a great effort?' Bart asked.

'Not even then.' She stood up. 'If you'll excuse me, I'm going to bed.'

Both men rose, and Bruce accompanied her to the door and followed her into the hall.

'Bart will be working on the script in the morning, which means I'll be free until early afternoon. Can I persuade you to take pity on my loneliness?'

'What form would the pity have to take?'

'Having lunch with me in Penzance.'

Samantha's first reaction was to refuse, but the spark of jealousy which Bart had shown earlier prompted her to agree.

'Call here for me at eleven,' she said. 'If the weather is good I'll prepare a picnic for us to have on the beach. It'll be better than sitting in a stuffy hotel.'

From the look on Bruce's face she felt he would have preferred the hotel, but he did not say so, and she went to her room knowing he was watching her until she was out of sight.

At midnight she heard a car drive away and a little while later Bart's steps sounded on the landing. They slowed momentarily outside her door and then moved on again, and she wondered if he had done it deliberately, and how she would have felt if he had knocked on the door and asked to come in. Afraid of the answer to this question, she burrowed her head into the pillows and fell asleep.

The few hours Samantha spent with Bruce next day were surprisingly pleasant. Without Bart around, he was far less flirtatious and was content to talk seriously with her on any subject she chose. Most of the time, however, they lay silently sunbathing, with an occasional dip into the sea which, despite the heat of the day, was still cold enough to make one catch one's breath.

'You're even lovelier in a bikini than fully clothed,' he commented as Samantha squatted on the sand to unpack the picnic basket. 'I can see why Bart thinks of you as a doll.'

'He doesn't like dolls,' she said, then remembering she was not supposed to have heard that conversation, hurriedly handed Bruce a plate of cold chicken and salad.

'I suppose it's because he's such a giant of a man,' Bruce mused. 'Men like that either go for very small or very tall women.'

'And Bart likes them tall,' she said.

'Too true!'

Samantha concentrated on her food, though her appetite seemed to have deserted her. But by the time she had drunk half a bottle of chilled Sancerre, she felt more cheerful and, reclining on her towel, realised with amazement that she had hardly thought about her business for several days.

It was because of Bart. She had been so busy thinking of him that everything else had faded into insignificance. It was a new experience for her to feel like this about a man, and she wondered if Bart had ever allowed a woman to affect him in the same way. Somehow she doubted it.

Sighing heavily, she sat up, and Bruce instantly opened his eyes.

'What a deep sigh, my lovely. You haven't fallen for our mutual friend, have you?'

The unexpectedness of the question was nearly her undoing. But not quite.

'He isn't my type,' she said flatly, and looked out to sea, unaware how childlike her profile was, with its wide, serene brow, retroussé nose and curving upper lip.

'It would be a shame if you were,' Bruce went on. 'He isn't the marrying kind and you quite obviously are.'

'What makes you think so?'

'It's written in your eyes.'

She half-smiled. 'I thought you were a friend of Bart's?'

'That doesn't mean I can't warn you about him. I'm probably one of his closest friends, yet if you asked me how well I know him, I'd have to confess that I don't. Only two people have that privilege—his father and Arthur.'

'What's his father like?' she asked, turning quickly.

'An older edition of Bart, to look at. But in character he's softer. Bart might despise his mother, but he's inherited a great deal of her determination. It gave him the backbone to make a writer of himself.'

'I though writers were born, not made.'

'Baden-Powell once said that writing is ten per cent inspiration and ninety per cent perspiration.'

'What did Bart's father do?' she asked.

'Not much. He inherited a fortune from an American uncle. Bart has no need to work either, but he's always refused to take a penny from his family. He wants to be his own man.'

'He's certainly succeeded.'

'Very much so. He's always maintained that one's strength lies in being self-reliant, which I suppose is why he considers it a weakness to be in love. Unlike me.' Bruce's hand reached for hers and he pulled her so sharply that she fell down upon him. 'I'd love to be in love with you.'

Before she could move, his hand came up to the back of her head and pressed her face down upon his. Their lips met and she tried to respond, wanting to feel some emotion but knowing it was hopeless. She might as well be kissing a stone. But the embrace had the expected effect on Bruce and she felt the surge of his body beneath hers.

'Come up to London next weekend,' he whispered. 'You can either stay with me or I'll book you into a hotel.'

'No, thank you.' Though her voice was quiet, there was a tone in it that silenced him.

He let her go and turned his face up to the sun. Samantha settled back, careful to keep a little distance between them. She was glad he had taken her rebuff so well, but also somewhat deflated. Did people in the film world treat sex so lightly that they could switch their emotions on and off like a tap? And was Bart the same? If he were, it was surprising he had not made some advances to her; unless he did not fancy her sufficiently even to try. Remembering the careless way he had kissed her, she decided this was the reason. To him she was a good scout; a young tomboy who had opted out of life and was content to live in a Cornish backwater.

It was four o'clock before Bruce and Samantha returned to the cottage, and as they ambled up the lane swinging the empty picnic basket between them, they heard the sound of a woman's laugh.

'Ah, Linda,' said Bruce. 'I'd recognise those silver-gilt tones anywhere. They match the colour of her hair.'

Silver-gilt was an apt expression to have chosen, though gilt was the word that came most strongly to Samantha's mind as she looked at the tall, slender girl reclining on a chaise-longue next to Bart. A bright parasol protected her from the sun, for she had the skin of a tea-rose, so delicate that it looked as if it had been painted on to her bones. Her features were perfect, with the clear lines of a classical sculpture, and though Samantha suspected that the curve of the upper lip was artificial, the colour was so skilfully applied that only a discerning eye could have known.

Bart was looking into the china blue eyes with such appreciation that it was hard to believe he had made any derogatory remarks about the girl the night before, and jealousy hit Samantha with unexpected force.

'Bruce, you beast!' Linda cried as he walked across the garden. 'How mean of you not to be here to greet me.'

Bruce bent to kiss her, then straightened and introduced Samantha. Linda's blue eyes took in the faded·jeans and sun top, and the silky black hair tossed by the breeze.

'So you're the little housekeeper Bart's been telling me about. I'm sure you haven't had much chance to do anything in the kitchen since Batman got here.'

'Batman?' Samantha echoed.

'Arthur,' Linda gurgled. 'Though sometimes I call him Mr Perfect. Either title fits him. No matter what you ask, he always manages to do it.'

'Which reminds me that I should go in and offer to help,' said Samantha, seeing this as a good excuse to leave.

No one tried to stop her and she went into the kitchen where Arthur was seated at a table chopping mushrooms.

'Are they for supper?' she asked.

'Yes, in a cream sauce with veal, and there's iced corn soup to begin with and strawberry tart to follow.'

'Is there anything I can do to help?'

'You could lay the table,' he said, 'and arrange the flowers. Mr Jackson mentioned how nice the vases look and I told him they were your work.'

Stupidly elated to know she had done something that pleased Bart, Samantha went into the dining-room and set the table, using white and gold place mats which looked exceptionally attractive on the rosewood table.

She was curious about Bart's house in Monte Carlo. All she knew was that it was built on terraced land overlooking the town, and that it had a large swimming pool and a magnificent view. He did not live there for more than six months of the year, and spent the coldest of the winter months in Los Angeles, and the three hottest summer ones in London. Undoubtedly his life was organised to perfection.

Until a short while ago Samantha would have said her own life was the same. As she laid the knives and forks, she wished she could turn back the clock and be in her own office, harassed by day-to-day problems and trying to fit twenty-five hours of work into twenty-four, but happily heart-free. She leaned against the edge of the table. She was heart-free no longer. Love, which she had never believed would come to her, had arrived when least expected, and towards the most unlikely man.

Almost as if she had conjured him up, Bart came into the dining-room, blinking in the gloom after the sunshine. 'Lay a place for yourself,' he said abruptly. 'You're not to eat in the kitchen any more.'

'I don't see why. It's kind of you, Bart, but I'm not one of your friends.'

'An enemy, then?'

'You know I didn't mean that.'

'I'm damned if I ever know what you mean. You're a strange girl, Samantha; a little water sprite that flits away when I try to touch it.'

Bart stood closer to her and Samantha could feel the heat of his body and smell the grass that clung to him. There was a sultry look in his eyes and she wished he would put his arms around her and hold her.

'Don't be taken in by Bruce,' he said abruptly. 'He falls for every pretty face.'

'I'm glad you think I've got one.'

'Don't fish with me, little one, or you might catch more than you bargained for.' He fidgeted with a place setting. 'That blue dress you wore last night did nothing for you. I can't understand it. It looked so attractive in the window.'

'It's a window dress,' she grinned. 'Not a Samantha one.' He looked puzzled and she said: 'All that flowing material and the frills swamped me. It would look much better if I cut off a couple of frills.'

'Then you'll ruin it completely.' He looked grim. 'That button you sewed on my shirt came off the minute Arthur washed it.'

Samantha giggled and Bart looked at her in surprise.

'Don't try to make me believe you sewed it badly on purpose.'

'I didn't know Arthur was going to wash the shirt immediately. I wanted you to wear it first and have the button pop again.'

'Did you indeed?'

His tone was silky, and his movements were equally smooth as one arm came around her waist and pulled her tight against him. Samantha's breasts were flattened against his chest and she felt his heart beating slow and steady. Far too slow, she thought despairingly, and was all the more astonished by the fury of his kiss.

There was no build-up to it, no tentative exploration. It was the kiss of an exasperated man brought to the point of explosion. But why was he in such a temper? She would have liked to believe it was because she had spent a few hours with Bruce, but knew that this was wishful thinking, and wondered if something connected with Linda had provoked it. Was he not as immune to the actress as he professed?

Bart's kiss increased in passion, but Samantha would not

let herself respond to it, and eventually he raised his head, his eyes staring sombrely into hers.

'You can't be that much of an iceberg,' he said softly. 'Why won't you kiss me back?'

'I don't like meaningless kisses.'

'I see. You're one of those women who want every touch to be significant.'

'Yes,' she said, angered by his disdain. 'Yes, I do. And I'm not ashamed of it, either. Keep your cynical attitude for yourself and your friends, but leave me to my dreams.'

'That's all they are,' he warned, 'dreams. And like all dreams they won't last. One day you'll grow up and be prepared to settle for reality.'

'You're idea of reality is my conception of cynicism,' she retorted. 'You write with such understanding of people, yet you don't seem to have any, outside of your books. Maybe your feelings have to be kept between covers where they can be controlled. It isn't that you doubt love, Bart. You're scared of it. You're afraid of commitment.'

'I have good reason to be.'

'Why? Millions of people fall in love and most of them are happy. I know your father wasn't, but even he recovered enough to marry again.'

'Are you offering yourself to me?' Bart asked, drawing her close again.

Samantha kept her body stiff, but she could not hold herself away from him, for he was too strong.

'Would you like to be the wife of Jackson Bart, the millionaire novelist?' he went on. 'Would you like a villa in Monte Carlo, an apartment in Eaton Square and a house in Beverly Hills? I'll never marry a career woman, little one, so you might be just what I'm looking for. Money doesn't mean anything to you or you wouldn't hibernate down here. So how about it?' His breath was warm on her temple.

'Are you proposing to me?' she asked, still holding herself stiffly.

'I asked you if you would care to be mistress of all my homes,' he said.

Mistress. The word echoed and re-echoed in her mind. Mistress. She should have known he would never give up his freedom entirely.

'I'll take good care of you,' he went on. 'You would have everything you wanted.'

'I'll take a rain check on it, Bart. I'll always know where to get in touch with you?'

'Sure,' he replied and, with an ease which disconcerted her, dropped his hands from her body and sauntered out.

Dumbly Samantha stared after him, her body still shaken by its contact with his, her lips still bruised by the hard pressure of his mouth.

'I hate you, Bart Jackson,' she whispered. 'I hate you!'

CHAPTER EIGHT

In the past Samantha had always dealt with any emotional problem by immersing herself in work. At the drawing board she found peace, and would stay there for hours until her worries faded away. But she could not bury herself in work here. Apart from which, she doubted if the drawing board would be the same palliative today that it had been in the past. Meeting Bart had completely changed her attitude to life.

Depressed by the knowledge of this, she went upstairs and rummaged in the drawer to find a book to read. Instead she found her box of colours and a drawing pad, and on an impulse she took them to the window seat and started to sketch her view of the garden. Unexpectedly Bart appeared, wandering slowly around the flower beds, pausing occasionally to touch a bloom. Then he settled in a deckchair and remained motionless, as if lost in thought.

Samantha included Bart in her drawing, putting a faint sardonic smile on his lips. Then she began to paint, using a large brush and a lot of water for the trees, and a smaller brush and less water for the grass, scribbling yellow against the green to show the sun-parched patches, and adding flecks of scarlet and pink for the flowers.

In three-quarters of an hour the picture was finished. Bart had long since gone, but she did not need to see his body in order to paint it. She carried the watercolour to her dressing table and left it there to dry while she went into the bathroom to shower. She had no doubt which dress she was going to wear this evening. It was the apricot one which she had designed herself, and which had been such a success in her last collection.

Suddenly she had an urge to telephone Carol and see how

103

things were going. There had been a production problem at one of the factories and they might need her advice. She moved to the door and then stopped. She dared not break her promise to Dr Fergusson. If she rang Carol once, she would do it again; and from there on it was but a short step to being in daily contact with her.

Yet the revival of her interest in work filled Samantha with elation, for it meant she was beginning to get better. And once she was fully recovered, she would be able to push Bart out of her mind and into limbo—where he belonged.

But for the moment he was firmly entrenched there, and she kept seeing his face as she brushed her hair and applied heavier make-up than usual to her eyes. Then she stepped into the apricot dress. Its colour enhanced the bloom in her cheeks and made her hair gleam like black satin. The dress might have looked shapeless on a hanger, but on a human figure it clung where it should, emphasising the body with a subtlety for which she was famous. For all its simplicity it made her look far more feminine than the blue frilled horror of the night before. Samantha put on a pair of narrow, plain court shoes, dabbed perfume behind her ears and went downstairs.

The open admiration on Bruce's face contrasted starkly with Bart's cool indifference. But Linda, elegant in a green and gold sari, gave her a look of ill-concealed dislike which assured Samantha that she was looking her best.

Bruce hurried forward with a drink. 'Champagne, Samantha?'

She nodded and accepted a glass.

'Each time I see you,' he went on, 'you look less and less like my idea of a housekeeper. I hate to think of you hiding your light under a Cornish bushel.'

'Don't try to entice Samantha away from here,' Bart interrupted, 'or you'll have Mrs Barclay coming after you. She regards Samantha as her little treasure.'

'She'd be my little treasure too, if she came to work for me.'

'I think it's wonderful to be domesticated.' Linda was not going to be left out of the conversation. 'I can't boil an egg without overcooking it.'

'Cooking isn't one of Samantha's strong points either,' Bart rejoined.

'Oh?' China blue eyes widened as they turned on Samantha. 'What do you do here, then?'

'Keep the house clean—and general duties,' Samantha said vaguely. 'Mrs Barclay is a light eater.'

'You wouldn't need to do any cooking whatever if you came to work for me,' said Bruce.

'I might have to do other things that I'd like even less!'

Bruce gave Samantha a hurt look but followed it up with a swift grin. Samantha grinned back, finding his flirtatiousness too open to be disturbing.

'I've been reading Bart's script.' Linda tried again to take over the conversation and, because she chose a subject which interested both the men, she succeeded. 'I agree with the alterations Bart has made, but I think the love scene can still be improved.'

'What do you think?' Bruce asked, turning to Bart.

'I like it the way it is. Linda's being subjective. She wants me to make Diana more sympathetic so that the audience will like her better.'

'Is that such a bad idea?'

'The whole essence of the story is that Diana is a tough little go-getter, but that Graham can't help loving her.'

'There's a difference between being a tough little go-getter and being despicable,' Linda pouted. 'And that's the way you've written her.'

'And the way I want you to portray her.'

'I'm tired of playing villainesses.'

'But you do it so well,' Bart said.

'Bart's right,' Bruce agreed. 'He wouldn't let me audition

anyone else for the role. He insisted I give it to you.'

'Angel!' Linda blew a kiss in Bart's direction and looked ready to purr.

Samantha found Bart's behaviour inexplicable. He had professed his desire not to rekindle his affair with the actress, yet he had recommended her for the leading part in his new film. It was impossible to believe no one else could have played the part equally well, and she wondered if this was his way of paying Linda for services rendered. Unless, of course, his protestations of not liking her were a defence against his real feelings.

Knowing how Bart felt about commitment, Samantha could easily believe that if he found himself in love, he would do everything in his power to persuade himself otherwise; even to the extent of rejecting the woman. Was this what he had done with Linda? And did he now regret it and wish to give her the coveted role of Diana as a peace offering?

These thoughts preoccupied Samantha during dinner and she found it an effort to eat the delicious food set before her. After the meal she disappeared into the kitchen and, ignoring Arthur's protests, she washed and wiped the silver cutlery, delaying as long as possible her return to the sitting-room.

When she did go back she was put out to see that her absence had gone unnoticed. Linda and the two men were still arguing over the script and Bruce apparently coming round to her point of view.

'Wait till I finish the whole script,' Bart finally exclaimed. 'Then if you still feel I should soften Diana, I'll do it. But not yet.'

'Fair enough,' said Bruce, and Linda gave in gracefully and smiled meltingly at Bart.

Samantha was curious to read the script they were arguing about, and decided to ask Bart later if she could do so. Of course he might feel about his writing the way she felt about her designs, and not want an outsider to see it until it was completed. She gave him a swift glance and then turned her eyes away from him. She could still not equate him with the man whose books she so enjoyed, and doubted if the two images in her mind would ever coincide.

At eleven o'clock Bruce and Linda stood up to return to the inn, and Linda grumbled at the inconvenience of not having a private bathroom.

'It's very rustic and pretty there, but it's so damned primitive.'

'They have posture-sprung mattresses and constant hot water,' Bruce protested. 'I'd hardly call that primitive.'

Samantha felt Bart's eyes on her and knew he was warning her not to suggest Linda stay here. Again she pondered on his reasons, but before she could come to a conclusion, Bruce spoke in her ear.

'Linda and I aren't going back to London till the afternoon. What are my chances of seeing you in the morning?'

'I'll be busy in the house. I didn't do anything here today.'

'I'm sure another day won't matter. Everything looks perfectly clean to me.'

'That's because you don't look in the corners.'

'Who lives in corners?' He caught her hand. 'I won't always let you run away from me, Samantha.'

His voice was still low and he seemed oblivious of the sardonic look Bart was casting in his direction. Linda looked amused too, and Samantha knew the actress was pleased that Bruce was flirting with her.

She wants Bart to think of me as one of Bruce's girl-friends, Samantha thought. She knows Bart will never fight for any woman; he doesn't consider them sufficiently important for that.

'I'll see you in the morning,' Bruce said firmly, and Samantha forced herself to concentrate on him. 'If you're still determined to work, I'll take a duster and help you.'

'I might hold you to that,' Samantha warned, and moved away from the front door as he and Linda walked down the path.

'You're a beast not to drive us back,' Linda called out to Bart.

'The walk will help you to keep your perfect figure.'

'I didn't think you still noticed it.'

Bart gave a sensuous chuckle but, as he closed the front door and went back to the sitting-room, Samantha saw that his eyes were unamused.

He was a hard man, she thought suddenly, and knew he could never be cajoled into doing something against his will. He had a first-class brain and it was unlikely that any woman would ever wind him around her finger. Yet love did the strangest things to the strongest of people, and if she could insinuate herself into Bart's life he might fall in love with her without realising it. After all, as Mrs Barclay's supposed housekeeper, Bart could never tell her to go.

She tried to envisage what her life would be like if Bart suddenly decided he loved her. How would he react to her fame and independence? It was a thought that brought so many problems with it that she gave a deep sigh.

'What's wrong?' Bart asked. 'A minute ago you looked like a cat who's swallowed a canary, and now you look as if it's given you indigestion.'

'It has,' she replied flippantly.

'Let that be a lesson to you, then. Little girls shouldn't eat food that's too rich for them.'

'I'm not a little girl.' She kept her voice pleasant. 'You shouldn't equate maturity with size.'

'Obviously Bruce doesn't,' Bart replied, picking up two copies of his script which lay on the settee. 'It's a long time since I saw him so taken with anyone.'

'Only because he knows I'm not attracted to him.'

'Why aren't you? He's good-looking, rich, possibly a bit too old for you, but——'

'Only ten years older—the same as you.'

'I'm much too old for you,' he said promptly. 'I'm too old for any woman.'

'Does Linda know that?' she asked evenly.

'Linda knows I don't want marriage.'

'Why did you recommend her for a part in your picture?' she asked. 'I thought you were trying to break with her.'

'I have broken with her. But she's still ideal to play Diana.'

'I'm sure she thinks you offered it to her as a sign of——'

'Not love,' he cut in swiftly. 'That's a sign I've never given to any woman.' He turned away abruptly, scripts in hand. 'And never will, either.'

He switched off the main light and only a standard lamp by the settee illumined the room. They both moved towards it at the same time and their hands met on the switch. A sharp tingle went up Samantha's arm and she drew back sharply.

'There must be a loose connection,' she lied, knowing it was the touch of Bart's hand that had caused the sensation.

'It was you and me,' he said bluntly, and stared at her intently. 'Didn't I see that dress in the window of that shop in Penzance?'

'Yes. You said you didn't like it and told me to get the blue one.'

'I remember now. I said it would make you look like a sack.' His eyebrows met above his dominant nose. 'It seems I was wrong. It does a damned sight more for you than that blue thing did. I can't understand it.'

She hid a smile. 'It's the way it's cut. A design should work with the material that's being used, not fight against it.'

'Spare me the reasons, child. I'll take your word for it.'

'I'm not a child,' she said tartly. 'Nor do you know everything about fashion.'

There was a sharp gleam in his sherry-brown eyes. 'You

enjoyed making that little point, didn't you? But then you
always enjoy trying to cut me down to size.'

'Only so that you don't tower over me,' she retorted.

'Like this, you mean?'

His arms came round her and his broad shoulders
blocked out the light. She knew he was using his strength
to show her he was master of the situation, and though she
wanted to protest, she was too weak to resist the desire
that flooded through her at his touch. His long, beautifully-
shaped hands moved slowly down her spine, pulling her
body towards him. Samantha melted within his hold, her
lips parting to receive his. He lowered his head, then surprisingly he stepped back, leaving her still trembling with
unfulfilled need.

'It won't do any good, Samantha,' he said softly. 'I've
had too many inoculations to succumb to the illness at this
stage of my life.'

She knew the illness he referred to was love, and that
it was pointless to argue with him.

'Once Bruce and Linda have left,' he went on, 'I want
to get my script finished. I've been working on it too long
already.'

With an effort Samantha made herself concentrate on
what Bart was saying. The passion that had swamped her
was receding, and the pride that replaced it gave her the
strength to speak to him as if what he had said was unim-
portant to her.

'I thought you didn't begin the screen play until you
came here?'

'Only the actual writing of it,' he explained. 'But it's
been stewing in my mind for months—since Bruce bought
the film rights from me. I have another book I want to do,
and I can't start on it until I've got this bloody thing out
of the way.'

'Are you telling me for any particular reason?' Samantha
asked, plumping up the cushions to ease her tension.

'Only so that you'll know I won't be good company in

the future. Peace and quiet are more important to me
than anything else.'

'I'll keep out of your way,' she promised.

'Good.'

With a casual nod he went out, and she stood for a
moment where she was. She wanted to run after him and
tell him he was a fool not to realise she was in love with
him, then decided that perhaps he did know it, and that this
was his way of telling her she was wasting her time.

Dejectedly she switched off the lamp and walked across
the hall. The light was on in the study and she heard the
sound of a typewriter. It stopped and then started again.
Well, whatever else she had done to Bart, she had not
affected his concentration. She would never have been able
to go to her drawing board and work as easily. That was
where women differed from men. They were rarely able to
divorce their business life from their emotional one. It was
not men who held back the progress of women, she
thought soberly, closing her bedroom door. It was women
themselves.

Samantha did not see Bart until noon next day, when
Linda and Bruce arrived at the cottage for an early lunch.
She did not want to eat with them, but Bruce came into
the kitchen and insisted she should.

Reluctantly Samantha followed him out to the garden.
An *al fresco* lunch was set out on the wrought iron table
on the terrace, and Linda, looking far less sophisticated but
even more beautiful in an oyster silk shirtwaister that almost matched her hair, was perched on the arm of Bart's
chair.

Seething with jealousy, Samantha noticed a lipstick mark
at the corner of Bart's mouth. She tried not to stare, but
he saw her look and casually took out his handkerchief and
wiped the smudge away. Samantha's jealousy sharpened
and she went to the table and busied herself unnecessarily,
rearranging the dishes.

'We'd better eat,' said Bart. 'Will you serve me, Linda?'

'Shouldn't that be my line, darling?' Linda laughed, and gracefully rose and approached the table. Standing beside the tall, slender blonde, Samantha felt like a pygmy.

'Will you serve *me*, Samantha?' Bruce called. 'I'd like a double portion of passion with some hot kisses on the side!'

'I'm afraid passion is off,' said Samantha, 'and the kisses are reheated ones. But I can offer you some cold heart and sharply pickled tongue!'

The two men laughed, but Linda's full mouth tightened and the look she gave Samantha was far from friendly.

'You're very lucky to have a post like this,' she said in an undertone. 'No one would guess you're only the house-keeper here.'

'That's why I stay,' Samantha said evenly. 'The day of the mistress and the servant has long since gone.'

'But not of the master and the mistress.' The voice was soft but the china blue eyes were hard. 'Don't get carried away with your importance here. Bart is mine.'

'Is he? I'd have said he was his own man.'

'That only shows how little you know him.' Thin hands, with very long pointed nails, hovered over the salad bowl, then picked it up and carried it across to Bart. 'I don't know how much you want of this, darling, so you'd better help yourself.'

Alone at the table, Samantha stared down at the dishes. She should be amused by the way Linda had spoken to her, yet she could not stop herself from feeling angry. A shadow fell across the table and she looked up and saw Bruce.

'What was Linda whispering to you about?'

'She was warning me off Bart.'

'I can understand why. I know he says he's finished with her, but I'm not sure it's true. My bet is that he still fancies her.'

Samantha refused to make any comment. She concentrated on filling Bruce's plate for him, then helped herself, hoping she would be able to swallow the food. A fine fool she was making of herself over Bart! She had come to Cornwall in search of peace and quiet and instead had found love and turmoil.

'You look different today,' Bruce commented. 'In that get-up I can visualise you waving the flag at a student rally!'

She looked down at the dust-covered shift she was wearing. It was another of her own dresses which she had bought in Penzance, and came from the range of beachwear which she had designed especially for an American wholesaler.

'Don't you like it?' she asked.

'I like it very much. Who made it?'

'It's a SAM dress.' She went over to a basket chair and sat down, choosing one that was furthest from Bart, who was eating his salad and meat with gusto. 'You're very interested in fashion all of a sudden.'

'Only because I'm wondering whom to get to do the clothes for my picture.'

'Is it all that important?'

'Everything's important in a film.'

'Don't expect Samantha to take much interest in clothes,' Bart drawled, showing he had been listening to the conversation. 'She's the least fashion-conscious female I've met.'

'I wouldn't have said that,' Bruce replied.

'You didn't see her before I took her in hand,' Bart informed him. 'Left to herself, she'd be happy wearing jeans for ever.'

'You could have fooled me.' Bruce was still eyeing Samantha. 'The dress you wore last night and the one you've got on today are very nice indeed.'

'They're both SAM dresses.'

'That's one of the designers I've short-listed,' Bruce said with satisfaction.

'To me, one dress is as good as another,' Bart intervened.

He caught Samantha's eye and looked completely unrepentant. 'Give or take a frill or two,' he added.

'If you want a designer for the film,' said Linda, 'how about Valentino?'

'I prefer SAM,' Bruce said firmly.

'What's so special about him?' Bart asked.

'It's a she,' Bruce answered, 'and according to Jacky—my wardrobe mistress—she's a phenomenon. A Mary Quant but with a wider appeal.'

'Does your—er—Jacky know her?' Samantha asked guilelessly.

'I don't think so. But as I said, she's put her top of the list.'

'You'd better hurry and finish your lunch,' Bart interrupted. 'If you miss your train, you'll have to take a slow one.'

'Heaven spare me from that,' said Linda, promptly rising. 'Come on, Bruce. You can feed your face when we're travelling.'

Goodnaturedly the producer set his plate on the table and a few minutes later was seated in the dark red Mercedes with Bart and Linda.

'I'll be seeing you, Samantha,' Bruce called, waving to her as the car glided away from the gate.

Samantha waved back, sure that he would, and equally sure that, on her part, it would lead nowhere.

She started to clear away the plates, trying not to feel sorry for herself because Bart had not invited her to go to the station with them. He would rather make the long return journey on his own than have her sitting beside him. It meant he was wary of her, of course, but that could come from his usual fear of commitment, and not mean anything more.

I was an idiot to fall for him, she told herself glumly. He's as much my idea of a Prince Charming as a skunk!

A vision of a slender, gentle-eyed man came into her mind, totally unlike the rough-haired giant who had swept into her life like a typhoon, and would as swiftly sweep out of it when the summer was over.

If she were sensible she would pack her bags and run a thousand miles away. She shook her head. Unfortunately she was not sensible. Women in love rarely were.

CHAPTER NINE

WHEN Bart had said he wished to concentrate on his work and did not want any interruptions, Samantha had not realised he meant it so literally. But on the very afternoon of his visitors' departure, she found only one place laid in the dining-room.

For the next four days she barely saw him, except for an occasional glimpse through the study window. The weather was glorious and she wondered how he could bear to stay indoors all day.

'Doesn't Mr Jackson ever find it necessary to relax?' she finally asked Arthur.

The man shook his head. 'When he gets into a book, he hates stopping until it's finished. I've sometimes known him go on like this for a month or more. Sometimes he'll go without sleep for forty-eight hours at a stretch.'

Next morning Samantha bumped into Bart at the foot of the stairs. To her surprise he looked as vigorous as usual, though he had lost some of his tan.

'Hello, Samantha.' He greeted her without any slowing of his pace.

'Hello, Bart. I . . . you've been working very hard.'

'I told you I would be.'

'I know. But it seems so silly.' She saw his eyebrows rise and added hurriedly: 'I don't mean silly that you're working, but that you should be doing it indoors. Why don't you take your typewriter on to the terrace? I'll keep away from the garden if you're working out there.'

'If I wanted to work outside, I'd tell you.'

His tone was polite but cool, reminding Samantha that in his eyes she was the housekeeper, and that he would have no hesitation in asking her not to go into the garden, if that was what he wished.

'Don't worry about me, Samantha,' he went on. 'I dislike women who fuss.'

They were harsh words with which to dismiss a suggestion kindly meant, and Samantha wondered if he had guessed that she loved him and was warning her to steer clear of him. Miserably she decided to heed his advice, and took great pains to keep out of his way.

In the mornings she helped Arthur in the house, then took a picnic lunch to the beach, where she spent the rest of the day sketching the ever-changing pattern of the sea. The restless colour of the water, one moment green, the next blue or turquoise or silver, gave her many ideas for fabrics from which dress designs seemed effortlessly to follow. At first she ordered herself not to think of work, but eventually she gave in, finding it easier to accept her Muse than to fight it.

She had been asked to do a cruise collection for a select New York store, and these designs would be ideal for dresses to wear on shipboard.

She bundled the sketches into an envelope and posted them off to Carol, with a note asking her to send them to the Lancashire mill who made most of their fabrics.

'Whatever happens, don't let anyone contact me here,' she ended her letter. 'I'm still incognito and having fun.'

'Fun' was not the best word to describe her life since Bruce and Linda had departed. Her physical health was definitely improving, but her emotional state was doing the reverse. She knew she had to take herself in hand, and that to go on thinking about a man who had made it clear he did not want her would only end in misery.

But as she walked back from the beach that evening and caught a glimpse of Bart by the doors of the french window, stretching his arms and yawning, her racing heart told her that forgetting him was going to be impossible. Even when dishevelled and tired he was still vibrantly attractive. He rubbed one hand through his thick hair and yawned again, looking like a huge, lazy lion in the mellow rays of the setting sun.

Resolutely Samantha opened the gate and walked down the path. Bart looked up, saw her and immediately moved further back into the room and out of sight. Her step faltered but she continued to walk, blinking back tears of hurt. She was crossing the hall towards the stairs when he called her.

'Come into the kitchen, Samantha.' His voice was almost obliterated by a sharp yelping noise which sounded like the barking of a dog.

Not sure if she had imagined it, she obeyed him and was amazed to see a large, bouncing puppy that looked like a cross between a Labrador and a Great Dane.

'Good heavens!' she exclaimed. 'What is it?'

'A dog, regrettably.'

The puppy, though tied by a leash to a kitchen chair, became so excited at seeing Samantha that it jumped up on its hind legs and leapt towards her, skidding across the tiled floor and yelping loudly when the chair refused to move as fast as he did.

'Oh, you poor little darling!' she cried, and bent towards it.

'Poor he may be, but little he certainly isn't,' Bart said icily.

'Then why did you buy it?'

'Buy it? Me?' Bart gazed heavenwards. 'Lord give me patience,' he muttered. 'The damned thing's yours. Don't you remember?'

Samantha thought furiously. She had not ordered a dog nor had she ever discussed buying one.

'How did it get here?' she parried.

'Some boy brought it. He said he came from a farm the other side of Folly's Wood, wherever that may be. He said he'd promised to let the housekeeper have it as soon as it was big enough to leave its mother.' Sherry-brown eyes stared at the puppy. 'It's my belief this beast was big enough to leave home the minute it was born!'

The animal in question, hearing the angry tones of the man, sat on the floor and started to whimper, straining at the leash and almost choking itself in its anxiety to be free.

'You're obviously not a dog-lover,' Samantha said crossly and, kneeling down, undid a collar that seemed far too heavy for the baby-soft fur.

'I happen to be extremely fond of animals,' Bart said icily. 'But I like them in their place and I like them to be trained.'

'You can't have a fully-trained dog without having an untrained puppy first.'

'Yes, you can,' he said firmly. 'I sent mine to an obedience school.'

'Which is obviously what you'd like to do with your women!'

'I don't reckon on keeping my women for the length of time I keep my dogs!' He spoke without rancour, as if he had made up his mind not to let her annoy him. 'Anyway, if Mrs Barclay doesn't mind you having the hound, I'm not the one to object.'

'Thank you,' she said pointedly.

'But keep it out of my way,' he concluded. '*And keep it quiet.*'

Almost as if he understood what the man was saying, the dog nuzzled against Samantha, his tail flailing her legs, his long wet tongue licking her hand as she bent to stroke his head.

'It's a darling,' she said, gazing into big, moist-brown eyes framed by lashes so long and fluffy that they looked as if they were made of cotton wool. 'Look at its lashes, Bart. Aren't they sweet?'

'Yes,' he said without bothering to lower his head, and strode out of the kitchen.

'Never mind, darling,' Samantha cooed, and caught the puppy up in her arms. It wriggled ecstatically, its tail wagging so fast that its body shook. 'I suppose Mrs Vivien must have ordered you,' she whispered into a silky ear. 'I wonder if she had a name planned for you? If she had, she might be upset if I christen you now. I'll just have to whistle when I want you to come to me.'

Arthur came in from the garden, holding a bunch of freshly-cut mint. 'Is there a basket around for the puppy to sleep in?' she asked.

'You're more likely to know about that than I am,' he replied.

She bit her lip, annoyed with herself for not being more careful what she said. If she were really the housekeeper she would undoubtedly know if there were any baskets on the premises.

'I thought you were using them to—to store fruit in,' she mumbled, making up the first story that came into her head.

'I'm using a wicker basket for the oranges and apples,' he agreed, 'but it would be too small for the dog. There's an old basket in the garden shed which might do. I'll fetch it for you.'

Arthur disappeared, returning after a short while with what looked like a real dog's basket, and Samantha wondered if Mrs Vivien had bought it in readiness for the puppy.

'What are you going to call him, miss?' Arthur asked.

Caught out, Samantha was silent. If she had any sense, she should have expected the question.

'I—I'm not sure. I'll wait to see what his character's like.'

The puppy was wriggling so much that she set him on the floor, whereupon he immediately scampered through the kitchen door to the hall. She ran after him, horrified to see him disappear into the study. How silly of Bart to leave the door open when he knew there was a young dog in the house.

'Come back!' she called, and raced into the room.

Bart was at his desk and the puppy was biting one of

his shoes. Bart tried to push him away with the other one, but the puppy thought it was a game, and with a happy growl fastened his teeth on the shoelace and shook his head furiously from side to side in an attempt to undo the bow.

'Will you get this bloody thing out of here?' Bart shouted.

Samantha scooped up the puppy. 'There's no need to shout! You'll frighten him.'

'Nothing will frighten that dog.'

This seemed to be true, for the puppy was wriggling ecstatically in Samantha's arms and licking her hand. 'That only shows you how good-tempered it is,' she said angrily. 'There's no need for you to bully it.'

'Him,' he said. 'It isn't an "it".'

Tightening her arm around the warm body, Samantha stalked out. She turned to close the door, but Bart was already there, shutting it firmly before she could do so. She almost expected to hear the key turn in the lock, but the slam of the door was warning enough and, muttering beneath her breath, she returned to the kitchen.

Arthur had cleaned the basket and lined it with an old sheet before placing it beside the dresser, away from any draughts. Samantha put the puppy into it, but he immediately jumped out.

'He'll take a bit of training,' Arthur said.

Samantha nodded, beginning to be worried. To her, dogs were cuddly creatures to be petted and taken for walks, but she knew nothing about their training. The puppy was looking at her, pink tongue lolling out of his mouth, his head on one side, ears long and floppy. Those aren't the ears of a Great Dane or a Labrador, Samantha thought impishly. There's a third strain there, and it could well be spaniel.

'I don't know what you're going to grow up into,' she commented, patting its head.

'You'd best call him Heinz,' said Arthur.

'He doesn't quite have fifty-seven varieties,' she protested. 'He's a little more aristocratic than that. I think I'll call him Campbell.'

'That's a good name for him,' Arthur beamed, and too late Samantha remembered she had not intended to christen the dog. But it was done, and Campbell he would have to remain.

'I'd better nip into the village and get some dog biscuits,' she said. 'That general store by the church stays open late. Will you look after Campbell while I'm gone?'

'I'll have to, won't I?' Arthur grinned.

Samantha returned from the village with a basket laden with half a dozen tins of dog meat, a box of dried biscuits, and an extra pint of milk, as well as a book called *All You Need to Know about Bringing Up Your Dog*. It all boiled down to common sense, she found, when she opened the book and started to read it. One had to treat the animal like a child, with a firm but gentle hand, insisting it did not display tantrums at mealtimes or bedtimes.

But it was at bedtime that Campbell was at his most naughty, for though he went down like a lamb at ten-thirty, he rose like a lion at midnight and proceeded to howl to prove it.

Samantha, normally a light sleeper, had taken the nightly pills recommended by Dr Fergusson, and Campbell was in full throat before she was sufficiently roused from sleep to push aside her blanket and totter across the floor.

She was by the foot of the bed, searching for her slippers, when there was a loud banging at the door and it was flung open by Bart. He was still in slacks and sweater and was carrying the puppy in front of him, its fat little body dangling.

'Take this little swine before I strangle it,' he said, and dumped it on the floor.

Campbell skidded across to her and greeted her rapturously, licking her bare toes and making her giggle.

'I don't find it funny to be disturbed in the middle of the night,' Bart grated.

'It isn't the middle of the night,' she replied. 'And you weren't even asleep.'

'I was working in the study,' he admitted. 'But I still want peace and quiet—which I won't get with that dog howling.'

'He's only crying because he doesn't like being left alone. But he'll get used to it after a couple of days.'

'If you think I'm going to have him howling for a couple of days, you'd better think again,' Bart said furiously. 'I've got a screen play to finish and I can't even *think* with a damned dog whining in my ears. Let him sleep here with you. I thought all women liked to have their pets in their rooms.'

'Two-legged ones only,' she replied sweetly.

The door slammed behind Bart and Samantha sank on to the bed. The puppy tried to jump up beside her, but the bed was too high and he collapsed to the floor in an ungainly golden heap.

'Lovely boy,' Samantha cooed, and picked him up. 'But I can't let you sleep here with me. If you get used to it, Mrs Vivien will never be able to leave you in the kitchen, and I don't think Mrs Barclay would like her housekeeper to keep a dog upstairs.'

Yawning, she stood up, slipped on her dressing-gown and went downstairs, carrying the dog close against her. The lights were off and in the darkened hall she glimpsed the gleam of light that came from beneath the door of the study. 'Sh-sh!' she said to the wriggling puppy, and carefully tiptoed to the kitchen.

Once there, she put the dog in his basket and held him down. The puppy resisted at first, then relaxed. But as soon as Samantha took her hand away, he bounded out, determined that he was not going to be left alone again.

'What a nuisance you are,' Samantha informed him, not meaning a word of it, and the puppy banged his tail on the basket and licked her hand. She knew she would have to stay beside him until he fell asleep, and she knelt by the basket and pulled the folds of her dressing-gown more closely around her.

'Hush now,' she soothed the animal, and went on talking to it in a gentle voice, patting its velvet smooth body and letting her hand rest on its round, warm tummy.

Campbell settled on the sheet and put his head down, occasionally licking her fingers to show he was still awake. Her legs grew stiff and the cool tiles on the floor started to chill her. But the sleeping pills were working again and gradually her words became slurred. Her body sank to the ground against the basket, and her shiny black hair splayed out upon the golden fur. The clock on the mantelshelf chimed. Samantha sighed in her sleep and the puppy snored contentedly.

A bright light shining down on her eyes awakened her. At first she did not know where she was. Her legs were numb, and as she tried to struggle to her feet, she felt firm hands lifting her into a standing position.

Suddenly she realised she was in Bart's arms. He was still wearing slacks and sweater but there was dark stubble on his chin, and a glance at the window told her that dawn was already breaking.

'Come on,' he said gently. 'You'll get pneumonia lying down there.'

'I had to stop Campbell from crying.'

'I know.' Bart's voice was unusually soft. 'But I don't think he'll cry now. He looks as if he's settled comfortably.'

Samantha glanced down and saw that the puppy was fast asleep, his forelegs splayed out, his head lolling against the side of the basket, one long ear dangling over the edge.

'Isn't he adorable?' she whispered.

'Adorable,' Bart echoed, but from the way his arms tightened around her, Samantha knew he was not referring to the dog.

'Bart,' she said huskily, and raised her face to his as a child would have done. Her longing for him to kiss her was so intense that she lost all inhibition. She loved this man and felt no shame in showing her need.

For several seconds he gazed at her, his eyes darkening until the gold in them seemed to disappear entirely. Then with a murmur he crushed her close. Samantha had never been more conscious of his strength than she was at that moment, nor more conscious of his gentleness, which made nonsense of his cynical façade.

His hands were warm and possessive, yet they remained firmly on her back, nor did he give her a passionate kiss, but seemed content to move his mouth across the smooth curve of her cheek, to nibble at her ear lobe and gently touch the side of her neck under the soft hairline. Then he twined his fingers among the silky tresses of her hair and buried his face in the fragrant dark cloud. His heart was beating fast and he was breathing heavily.

'Darling Samantha, you're so. . . .'

He sought her mouth, parting her lips and gently probing with his own. Passionately she responded, knowing she wanted to be possessed by this magnetically vital man. They were feelings she had never before experienced, and they changed her from a cool-headed, ambitious career girl to a primeval woman at the mercy of her biological needs.

'Bart,' she whispered blindly, 'I want you.'

His trembling body told her he had heard the words, and his hands touched her throat, then moved down to cup her breasts. She twined her arms around his shoulders, willing him to pick her up, not caring what he did as long as he did not leave her.

'Samantha, stop it!' His words were like a cold douche of water, and he pulled her hands firmly down to her sides and pushed her away from him. 'It's late. We must go to bed.' His eyes narrowed. 'Alone, Samantha. I don't want any complications with you.'

She stared up into his face. 'You're scared of me, aren't you, Bart?'

'I'm scared of all women.'

He went to the kitchen door and held it open for her. She glanced down at the puppy, still sleeping peacefully, then slipped out of the kitchen. At the foot of the stairs she waited for Bart, and they mounted the steps side by side.

'I've got to finish my script,' he said flatly. 'And if I can't do it in peace here, then I'll have to go somewhere else. Do you understand what I'm saying?'

'Perfectly. But after you've finished the script—what then?'

'We'll see,' he replied enigmatically and, touching her cheek with one finger, he went across the hall to his own room and closed the door firmly behind him.

CHAPTER TEN

SAMANTHA did her best to keep Campbell out of Bart's way but, as if he were possessed of the devil and had been sent there to try them, the puppy managed to thwart all her efforts.

Two days after Bart's threat that he would leave the house if he did not have sufficient peace to finish his script, Campbell got into his bedroom and played havoc with his ties, completely chewing through one and mauling several others. It was Arthur's fault for leaving the door ajar, but Bart vented his wrath on Samantha.

'You can't keep a puppy on a leash permanently,' she protested, when called into his room to see the damage Campbell had done. 'Nor can you expect to have a puppy without things like this happening.'

'As I didn't expect to *have* a puppy,' Bart said icily, 'I'm damned if I'm going to put up with it.'

'What do you want me to do, kill him?'

Bart's jaw tightened ominously. 'Control him. Dogs, like women, enjoy being kept on a tight rein.'

'You're thinking of horses,' Samantha said serenely.

But Bart was too infuriated to be amused, and stormed out of the room.

Mutinously Samantha picked up the mangled ties and Campbell jumped up playfully to catch one of them.

'I suppose you might as well finish them off,' she told him, then changed her mind, afraid that if she allowed the puppy to chew these, he might go in search of others. Catching Campbell by the scruff of his neck, she gave him a sharp slap on the rump and led him downstairs.

'You're a naughty boy! You're not to go upstairs any more. Do you understand me?'

'Woof,' Campbell agreed, and immediately bounded up the stairs again.

Samantha dived after him and managed to catch him by the tail. He gave an indignant yelp, but she ignored it and, lifting him in her arms, carried him out the garden. She left him happily rolling on the grass, then went into the kitchen, firmly closing the garden door behind her.

'There's a letter for you,' said Arthur. 'It's on the table.'

It was a short note from Mrs Vivien, saying she was feeling much better and hoped Miss Rose would tell her when she could return to the cottage. 'I'm getting restless and don't like neglecting my job for so long,' was the plaintive postscript.

Samantha knew she would have to let Mrs Vivien come back in a couple of weeks. But before then she would have to reveal her true identity to Bart.

She tried to imagine his reaction and felt disturbed by the thoughts that came into her mind. Would his fear of becoming involved with her increase when he realised she was a brilliant and successful dress designer, and not a simple, unpretentious girl?

She was terribly afraid that the occasional tender feelings he had shown towards her might disappear completely; and with tenderness gone, his resolve not to fall in love with her, might send him scurrying away. Her only hope was that he would grow so fond of her in the next two weeks that he would not have the heart to let them part.

For the next two days Samantha kept the puppy with her. She took him to the beach and taught him how to play with a ball and bring it back. He was quick to learn, and was soon retrieving sticks and stones and placing them at her feet for her to throw again.

On the third day the long spell of fine weather broke. Wind lashed at the trees and rain beat down on the windowpanes. Unable to go out, Samantha decided to do a watercolour of the sitting-room, showing the bay window and

Mrs Barclay's pretty bureau. Campbell was snoozing in his basket in the kitchen and she did not expect any trouble.

Within a short time she became immersed in her painting, using a dry brush technique which meant working slowly and with great care. At one point she thought she heard someone walking down the garden path, but paid no heed, and went on with her painting until it was finished an hour later.

There were footsteps on the path again, and this time she went to the window and peered through the driving rain. Bart was coming in through the front gate, his long-legged stride sending up sprays of water. He disappeared round the side of the house and she heard him go into the kitchen, probably to take off his soaking mackintosh. Then he crossed the hall and entered the study. But he did not close the door and she waited, tense without knowing why.

Suddenly there was a loud bellow of rage. 'Samantha! Samantha, will you come here *at once*!'

Heart sinking, Samantha obeyed the call. As she reached the door, Campbell shot past her, ears back, tail extended. He skidded on the hallway floor, regaining his balance and bolted into the kitchen.

In horror, Samantha entered the study and looked down at the floor. Chewed-up pieces of paper lay scattered on the rug, and she knew immediately that they were part of Bart's script.

'You m-must—someone m-must have left the door open,' she stammered. 'Campbell couldn't have got in here otherwise.'

'I thought I told you to keep him on a lead.' Bart's voice was menacing in its quietness. 'Do you know how many pages he's ruined?'

Without answering, Samantha bent and scrabbled wildly at the pages, trying to gather up as many pieces as she could.

'Stop it!' Bart exclaimed furiously. 'What the hell do you think you're doing?'

'Some of these can be sellotaped together,' she replied. 'I'll do it myself.'

'You'll do nothing of the sort,' he exploded. 'All I want is for you to get out of this room and get out of my life. I've had as much of you as I can stand.'

'You can't blame me for the dog,' she protested.

'Who else should I blame? He's yours, isn't he?' Bart's voice rose. 'I warned you to keep him under control, but you must be deaf as well as stupid!'

Calmly ignoring him, though her heart was pounding like a piston, Samantha went on retrieving the tattered pages. Then she stood up, carried them to the desk and put them beside another neatly stacked pile of papers. Glancing down, she suddenly noticed that the waste-paper basket had been overturned, and that crumpled pieces of quarto-sized paper lay around it.

Angrily she swung round to Bart. 'Campbell didn't eat your script,' she flared. 'He just knocked over your waste-paper basket and chewed up the paper you'd thrown away.'

For a moment Bart looked taken aback, then relief softened his features—but only for an instant—making it quite clear he was not yet ready to forgive her.

'Whether they were discarded papers or not is beside the point,' he stated. 'The dog had no business being in here. Today it was the waste-paper basket. Tomorrow it may be the manuscript. I'm not going to warn you again. Either you get rid of that dog or I'm leaving.'

'Leave, then!' she flared. 'Do you think I care?'

'Mrs Barclay might. I'm a guest of hers.'

'And the rudest, most bad-tempered one she's ever had!'

Samantha had reached the end of her tether. 'Ever since you arrived here you've been bullying me and behaving as if you're the master of the house. But as you've just re-minded me, Mr Jackson, you're only a guest. And guests normally show respect for the people who live in a house.'

'Like you, I suppose?'

'Like me. Mrs Barclay knew the dog was coming here and I'm sure she also knew that puppies often damage things. But she wanted me to be happy—that's why she agreed to let me have him.'

'Meaning I should allow him to eat my papers, chew my ties and generally make a bloody nuisance of himself?'

'Keep your hyperboles for your film scripts,' she snapped.

Furiously Bart took a step towards her, and Samantha recoiled in fright.

'Don't worry,' he said harshly, 'I don't think much of women, but I've never yet hit one.'

'Because you've so much self-control?' she asked sarcastically. 'Or because you know how vulnerable they are?'

'Women are as vulnerable as scorpions!' he retorted. 'The more fragile they pretend to be, the more dangerous they are.'

'Thanks.' Samantha's voice was shaky. 'You really do have a high opinion of my sex.'

'I have no opinion of them. I thought I'd already made that clear. Women are out for everything they can get.'

'And what am I out for?' she demanded.

'Me,' he said bluntly. 'But I'm not available, so you can lock up that damned dog of yours and stop hoping that a golden puppy will find its way to my heart.'

'You don't have a heart,' she cried. 'You've got a typewriter instead!'

'You'd better believe it,' he agreed, and turned his back on her.

Blindly she ran out. Arthur was in the kitchen and she could hear him talking to the puppy. She moved towards them and then stopped, knowing she could not bear Arthur's questions. She needed to put as much distance as she could between herself and Bart. He was not normal in his attitude to women and she had been crazy to think he was.

Wrenching open the front door, Samantha ran into the garden. The rain was teeming down, but she ignored it and scurried along the path to the lane.

Head down, she rushed onwards, making for the beach and the seclusion of a small cave she had discovered there. The wind beat against her trousers and the rain soaked through her thin sweater, flattening it against her skin. Soon her hair was plastered to her head in snaky coils. Water streamed down her face and she constantly had to blink her eyes in order to see.

But she resisted the temptation to return to the cottage. She wanted to be alone to think things out, to face the realisation that she loved a man who did not exist. She had fallen for a handsome body and a cool, sharp mind. The other virtues she had given him were figments of her imagination. In reality Bart was unloving, hard and selfish. It was a miracle that he was able to give such a different impression in his books.

A crash of thunder reverberated above her and lightning jagged its way across the sky like a devil's prong. Samantha looked up, half expecting Bart's face to be mirrored there, but all she saw were dark scudding clouds and torrential rain. Distracted by the storm, she did not notice the deep ruts in the lane and suddenly tripped and fell. Her hands and knees were badly grazed and there was a sharp pain in her shoulder. But she pulled herself up and went to walk again.

An agonising pain stabbed at her ankle and she gasped and stopped, afraid she was going to faint. Slowly the throbbing eased and she turned back towards the cottage. After taking a few steps, the pain was so intense that jagged points of light were dancing in front of her eyes and she sank to the ground again. She had no hope of walking. She would have to crawl.

Slowly she inched forward. The pain in her ankle and shoulder made her feel nauseous, and sweat poured down her face. She did not know how near she was to the cottage;

was it around the next bend or was there another stretch of lane before she reached the gate?

A big puddle lay ahead of her and she moved to the left, catching her hair in an overhanging bramble as she did so. Tears of frustration and fury filled her eyes and she collapsed in the mud. As she did so, her hand struck a sharp stone and she screamed loudly, suddenly aware that the skin of her palms was grazed and bleeding from dragging herself across the ground. It was impossible for her to move another inch. She would have to stay here until someone found her.

Samantha was semi-conscious by the time that happened. She was vaguely aware of Bart bending over her and lifting her up, and felt a deep sense of comfort at being cradled in his arms like a baby as he strode back to the cottage.

'You're mad!' he said, his voice almost inaudible, for the wind was still whipping round them. 'Mad. If Arthur hadn't gone to your room to look for you, you would have been out here all night. Don't you have any sense?'

But Samantha was too exhausted by pain to reply, and she lay silent against him, conscious only that in the warmth of his arms she had finally come home.

CHAPTER ELEVEN

SAMANTHA had no clear recollection of the next few hours. She knew Bart carried her back to Gable Cottage and up to her bathroom, where he sat her on the stool and gently undid her sandals, taking extra care with the one on her injured foot.

'It doesn't look more than a sprain to me,' he murmured, 'but I know they can be extremely painful.'

He was still speaking as Arthur came in with a glass of brandy. Without any protest, Samantha drank it, noting with surprise that Bart downed a glass too. It was only then that she saw he was as wet as she was, and she guessed he had been walking in the rain looking for her for some time. But when she asked about it, he merely grunted and started to run hot water into the bath.

'Do you think you can manage to get out of your clothes and into the water?' he asked.

'I think so.'

'If you aren't sure, I'll stay here and help.' He saw the colour flame into her face. 'For God's sake, don't be embarrassed,' he said angrily. 'I've seen nude women before and one more won't make any difference.'

'It makes a difference to me,' she retorted with the first show of spirit since her accident.

'Then I'll wait outside the door. If you have any problems call me. If I don't hear any sounds of splashing I'll come in and make sure you haven't fainted again.'

He went out, closing the door sharply behind him.

Gingerly Samantha began to undress. The pain in her shoulder had eased, so there was no problem with her tank top. It was more difficult to take off her jeans, for she was afraid of jogging her ankle. But eventually she managed it, and carefully eased herself into the bath, holding on to the rail as she lowered herself into the water.

It was bliss to feel it lap against her skin and she was tempted to soak for a long while. But the tiredness that overwhelmed her made her fearful of falling asleep and drowning—or waking up with a cry and having Bart dash in to save her—and she hurriedly began to wash herself.

Her ankle had ceased throbbing, although a sharp jab of pain shot up her leg as she climbed out of the bath and reached for the towel. When she was snugly wrapped in its thick folds she called to Bart to come in.

He did so at once, looming large beside her.

'As soon as you're dry, I suggest you put on a night-dress and I'll carry you to bed.'

'I can manage on my own,' she said quickly. 'It isn't far for me to hop.'

'There's no need for you to do that,' Bart replied, and gave a loud sneeze.

'You'd have done yourself more good if you'd had a hot bath too,' Samantha said crossly, 'instead of waiting outside my door. For heaven's sake go and have one now, before you end up with pneumonia. I'm perfectly capable of getting myself to bed.'

Silently Bart turned and left her, and Samantha waited until she heard his bath water running before she gingerly hopped into her bedroom. Arthur had thoughtfully put an electric pad between the sheets, and she snuggled against the heat and was soon fast asleep.

It seemed hours later when a knock on the door woke her up. Arthur came in with a tray and a delicious smell of roast chicken tickled her nostrils.

'Is it supper time already?' she asked.

'It's nine o'clock, miss. You've been dead to the world for hours. Mr Jackson was getting worried.'

'Where is he?'

'In the study. I told him to stay in bed, but he wouldn't listen.'

'He's obstinate,' Samantha said.

Arthur sniffed a reply. 'I'll be up later with a hot drink,' he said.

Samantha sat up in bed and tucked into the chicken and delicately cooked vegetables. Arthur had a way of making everything taste delicious. He prepared even better meals than her own housekeeper. Or perhaps she was more conscious of food now she was not working. In London she was sometimes barely aware of stopping for a meal, let alone of the food she swallowed.

Samantha mused on her way of life. It was not as if she had been so greedy for money and success that she had deliberately rejected pleasure. Enjoyment of life had always been important to her, but somewhere along the way the enjoyment had disappeared, crushed by the responsibilities of running a large business.

Yet if she never went back to the office, someone would keep the business going. After all, this was what she had trained her management to do. Accepting this fact, her dream of retiring seemed more reasonable, and she wondered why she did not accept one of the many excellent offers she had received from American and British firms eager to buy her out. She thought of the last offer she had turned down.

It had come from a huge American textile company, who had promised to run the business side of her operation if she agreed to design fabrics and clothes for three collections every year. They had also guaranteed to supervise the marketing of the other products to which she gave her name: make-up, bedlinen, scent, health foods.

'You name it, we'll sell it for you,' the President of the American concern had told her. 'We'll keep on all your employees if that's what you want. You'll have fame and cash without any administrative worries.'

Of course she had rejected the idea. At that stage of her life she had enjoyed being in control of everything. Now she was not so sure. It would be fun to spend her whole time doing the thing she loved best—designing. She would not be tied to an office, and she would be able to travel and live where she liked.

But all she liked was to live with Bart.

Her eyes brimmed with tears. Bart was attracted to her, but he did not love her. It was foolish to think otherwise. Even if he were willing to have an affair with her, she would be crazy to agree to it. Sooner or later he would want to move on to pastures new, leaving her with a shattered life that might take her years to put together again.

A rap at the door made her start up, and breathlessly she called out: 'Come in.'

Bart did so. He was carrying a transparent plastic bag which contained scissors and several bandages.

'I've come to strap your ankle,' he said, and obediently she slid it out from under the eiderdown. It was throbbing dully and a bruise was already beginning to show on the puffy skin.

'Isn't it a bit late to bandage it now?' she asked. 'I should have put on an ice bandage as soon as I came home.'

'It would still have been too late. Swelling had already started. But if I bandage it now, it will stop you from moving it inadvertently.'

With deft fingers he wound the bandage round her ankle. Samantha winced several times but knew he was being as careful as possible. It was uncanny that a man so big could work so gently. She looked at his downbent head and noticed that the hair on the nape of his neck was darker than at the front, and less curly too. He had a strong neck, the skin tanned to the colour of teak, which made her suppose that in Monte Carlo he must type in the garden with his back to the sun.

He straightened and drew away from the bed. 'You look none the worse for your escapade,' he said. 'You're lucky to have come out of it with only a twisted ankle.'

'I suppose you think I behaved foolishly?'

'Childishly,' he corrected. 'But then you *are* a child.'

'Why must you always harp on the difference in our ages?'

'Because you make me feel so much older than you. I suppose it's because you've led such a quiet country life.'

She almost told him that usually her life was as busy and exciting as his, but knew that now was not the time. Instead, she sank back on the pillows, her hair fluffing out around her, black as jet against the white linen.

'Will you kiss me goodnight?' she asked greatly daring.

'You're not such a little girl after all,' he said drily and, turning abruptly on his heel, strode out.

Instead of being upset, Samantha was delighted. Bart had probably made love to so many women that a casual goodnight kiss would mean nothing to him. The fact that he had refused her invitation told her more clearly than ever that he was afraid of her.

The bandage made her leg throb more painfully and her sleep was fitful. She awoke at six-thirty to find the birds in full song. Clambering out of bed, she hobbled to the window and curled up on the window seat. Head against the glass, she let her thoughts drift. Inevitably they went to the man who lay sleeping less than ten yards from her, and she dreamed of lying beside him and rousing him to desire.

She must have dozed off again, for when she awoke the sun was warming the window pane. Carefully she dressed, then went down the stairs, holding firmly to the banister for support.

The smell of frying bacon greeted her at the kitchen door, and Arthur turned from the stove and looked at her reprovingly.

'I was going to bring your breakfast up to you, miss.'

'That was a kind thought, Arthur, but I'm not an invalid.'

'That's more than I can say for Mr Jackson,' commented Arthur.

'What's the matter with him?'

'He had a very restless night. I heard him come down to

get some brandy, so I got up and made him a hot drink.
He has a nasty chill.'

'Oh lord,' Samantha said guiltily. 'It's my fault.'

Arthur did not contradict her. He placed some bacon,
sausages and grilled mushrooms on a warm plate and
brought it to the table.

'Do you think Mr Jackson would mind if I went up to
see him?' she asked, as she began to eat.

'He hates people fussing over him when he isn't well,'
Arthur replied. 'But he's even more upset if no one takes
any notice of him!'

Samantha smiled. 'You make him sound very contrary.'

'In some respects he's like a child. Men of great talent
often are.'

'What about women of talent?'

'I don't have any experience of them,' Arthur replied.
'I've met some of Mr Jackson's actress friends and a few
women writers, but I can't say I know them well. I really
prefer ordinary girls like you.'

Samantha hid a smile, wondering what Arthur would say
if he knew her true identity.

'I'll take Mr Jackson's breakfast up to him if you like,'
she said.

'He may be a bit bad-tempered,' Arthur cautioned. 'Wait
till later in the morning. I don't like the sound of his
cough, as a matter of fact. It's my belief he should see a
doctor.'

'Then I'll ring Dr Baxter,' Samantha replied instantly.

Arthur did not argue with her and she went to the
telephone as soon as she had finished her breakfast. Dr
Baxter said he would call at ten o'clock, and Samantha
hobbled to the garden gate to meet him.

'Please don't tell Mr Jackson who I am,' she said hurriedly. 'He thinks I'm Mrs Barclay's housekeeper. It's a
little joke I'm playing,' she went on, seeing the doctor's surprise. 'I'll tell him the truth before Mrs Vivien returns.'

'It seems an odd joke to me,' Dr Baxter replied, entering

the front door and going towards the stairs.

It was twenty minutes later before he came downstairs again. 'Mr Jackson has a high temperature and I've given him an antibiotic injection. He must take two tablets every four hours night and day for the next three days.'

'Is he seriously ill?' she asked fearfully.

'He would have been, if you hadn't called me in when you did. But I think I've managed to persuade him to stay in bed—for today at least.'

'I'll tell Arthur to take his clothes out of his room.'

'You needn't bother doing that,' Dr Baxter smiled. 'If he tries to get dressed he'll fall over!'

Filled with tenderness at the thought, Samantha hobbled up to see Bart. Anticipating that he would be feeling sorry for himself, she was surprised to find him in a furious temper.

'Who sent for the doctor?' he snapped. 'I know it wasn't Arthur, because he wouldn't dare do so without my permission.'

'It was me,' she confessed. 'I didn't fancy having one of Mrs Barclay's guests dying on my hands.'

'It will take more than a chill to kill me.' He gave a rasping cough, and for a moment his face was full of pain. 'How the hell can I finish my script if I have to stay in bed?'

'Why not let Arthur bring your typewriter up here? You could put it on the breakfast tray.'

'I'm in no mood to type.'

Bart coughed again, a severe bout this time, that left him looking wan, despite the red flush of fever which lay over his cheekbones. It was astonishing how illness had changed him. He seemed much older, with his eyes sunken and a drawn expression on his face. Sweat dampened his hair and his long sideburns had formed into curls.

Samantha longed to hold him close and press his leonine head to her breast. It was a maternal feeling which she had never before experienced towards a man and, realising that such deep tenderness made her very vulnerable, she was afraid.

'Would you like me to give you a cool wash?' she asked.

'Arthur's already done so.'

'A cool drink, then?'

'Arthur's given me one.' Bart scowled. 'There's nothing you can do for me that Arthur can't do better.'

'Really?' Samantha said drily.

'Very funny,' Bart growled, and started to cough again.

He reached for the box of Kleenex on the bedside table, but it fell to the ground. Samantha picked it up and handed it to him. The violent coughing continued for another minute, and when it ended, Bart sank back on the pillows, his eyes closed in exhaustion.

'Leave me alone,' he said in a thin voice. 'I can't bear people watching over me as if I were a corpse.'

Quietly Samantha went out.

Arthur was in the kitchen and would not be able to hear if Bart called, so she fetched a book and settled in a chair on the upstairs landing. She knew she would have no peace of mind if she were out of earshot.

Slowly the time ticked by. It was warm on the landing, although the front door was open. Occasionally a slight breeze drifted up, fragrant with the smell of roses.

Samantha was beginning to doze off when she heard a weak cry. Quickly she went into Bart's room and found him standing in the middle of the floor, swaying from side to side.

'What on earth are you doing?' she cried.

'Going to the bathroom.'

'You're walking towards the window.' She took his arm, and he staggered against her, nearly knocking her to the floor. A swift pain shot up Samanth's leg and she winced.

'Sorry,' Bart mumbled. 'It's your ankle, isn't it? I forgot to ask you how you were when you came in earlier.'

'I'm fine,' she replied quickly, and led him towards the bathroom. 'I'll wait out here for you,' she said, closing the door behind him.

When he emerged, he had made some attempt to comb his hair, but he had brushed it the wrong way and the curls at the front were more riotous than ever. Stubble lined his chin, but it was lighter than she had expected—almost golden—and she thought he must have had fair hair as a child.

Slowly she led him to a chair. 'Sit there while I make the bed more comfortable,' she ordered, and straightened the sheets and plumped up the pillows.

At last Bart was back in bed again, stretching beneath the counterpane with a sigh of relief.

'I'll draw up a chair and sit beside you,' Samantha told him.

Bart watched her in silence. His eyes glowed so brightly that they looked like lamps. Then his lids came down and his hands relaxed on the coverlet, the long fingers uncurling. For more than an hour he slept, and did not stir until Arthur entered the room with a glass of water and a bottle of pills.

'I didn't know you were up here, miss,' he said.

'I didn't like to leave him alone.'

'Don't talk about me as if I'm not here.' Bart's voice sounded firmer and, when he lifted his head, his eyes were more alert. He swallowed his pills but refused an offer of lunch. 'When a dog is sick it likes to be left alone,' he muttered, 'so get out and stop bothering me.'

Quietly Arthur left the room, but when Samantha rose to follow, Bart stopped her.

'Not you. Even sick dogs don't send their fleas away!'

It was hardly a compliment but it was more than Samantha had hoped for, and she settled back in her chair and continued her vigil. For the rest of the day and evening Bart slept, awakening only for a bout of coughing and to take his pills. At midnight Arthur suggested Samantha should go to bed, and promised to set his alarm for four a.m. so that he could give his employer his next dose of antibiotics.

'I'll do it,' Samantha replied, and there was something in her voice that told Arthur not to argue.

It was in the four hours from twelve till four, that Samantha felt closer to Bart than at any other time since she had met him. To watch him sleep through the night gave her the feeling that he belonged to her. She knew it was stupid to think this way, for he belonged to no one.

At four o'clock, when she woke him to give him his pills, he did not seem to recognise her, and he sank back into a far heavier slumber than before. For a moment she was afraid he was getting worse, and she placed her hand on his forehead. It was much cooler than she had expected, though his skin was damp and his pyjama jacket soaking wet.

Rummaging in a chest of drawers, Samantha found some fresh pyjamas. Bart seemed to have an inordinate amount of underwear, all of it pure silk. The pyjamas were in the middle drawer. There were at least six sets, all in vibrant colours, and all with his initials embroidered on the pocket.

She took out a cherry red jacket and waited a few minutes until he stirred again. Then she gently woke him up. Laboriously she removed his soaking jacket, wiped his chest and shoulders with a towel, and put on the dry jacket. Bart was far from pleased at being disturbed, and flailed his arms around like a rag doll whose stuffing was loose. But within a few seconds he was sleeping again, his breathing stertorous.

Every half hour Samantha got up and touched his forehead. He was still cool and no longer damp, but it was six o'clock before she could relax. Exhausted, she fell asleep and did not awaken until Arthur came in at eight a.m.

'You go off to your room and lie down,' he whispered. 'I'll sit with the master, if it will make your mind easier.'

'I think he's much better,' Samantha replied quickly.

'Perhaps if you could persuade him to have a light breakfast —orange juice and an egg perhaps.'

'I'll look after him. Don't worry,' Arthur smiled.

Samantha was too tired to smile back. She staggered to her room, collapsed into bed and instantly fell into a deep, dreamless sleep.

CHAPTER TWELVE

IT was well past noon when Samantha returned to Bart's room. She had awakened feeling considerably more refreshed, and on her bedside table found a glass of fresh apple juice, a thermos of coffee, and some pâté and toast wrapped in a napkin. Arthur's more than a treasure, she thought, sipping the juice and eating the delicious pâté, he's an angel.

Afterwards she washed her face and changed into one of the SAM dresses she had bought in Penzance. She had not worn it before and she hoped Bart would appreciate how subtly the lavender blue went with her grey eyes. It was another one of her favourite designs, with a heart-shaped neckline and a scalloped hem.

Samantha was pleased to see she was not as thin as she had been when she first arrived in Cornwall, though she could still gain several pounds without being overweight. Quietly she entered Bart's room, stopping in surprise when she saw a music stand balanced on the tray which was set across his lap. There was a pile of manuscript on the tray and a pen in his hand.

'Hello, Samantha.' His voice and expression were back to normal, as was his colour.

'You look much better,' she said, hurrying over to the bed.

'I feel it. I believe you stayed up with me all night? It wasn't necessary, you know.'

'I wanted to do it.'

His mouth lifted derisively and then straightened again, as if he had decided not to say something wounding.

'Should you be working?' she asked.

145

Instantly he scowled and she knew she had said the wrong thing.

'I just thought your mind might be a bit muzzy,' she murmured.

'Bart Jackson with a muzzy mind is still a damned sight sharper than most authors,' he retorted.

'I'm glad you're not conceited,' she said sarcastically.

'I don't happen to think it's conceit to know one's abilities. And I'm also aware of my faults.'

'I didn't think you admitted to any.'

'Which means you'd like me to enumerate them, I suppose?' He put his pen on the tray. 'I'm quick-tempered; I like my own way; I don't suffer fools gladly, and I consider personal freedom the most important thing in one's life. This latter opinion is considered to be my biggest fault, since it makes me a difficult man for a woman to trap.'

'I doubt if they'd be so keen if you weren't successful and rich,' Samantha snapped.

'You mean *you* only love me for my money?'

'What makes you think I love you?'

'I used the wrong word,' he said. 'But you clearly find me attractive.' One thick dark eyebrow lifted. 'You do find me attractive, Samantha, so don't bother frowning at me. I don't have any fear of admitting that I'm attracted to *you*. We both felt it the moment we met. If I had any sense I would have left the house immediately.'

'You can't blame me for being attracted to you,' she said as lightly as she could. 'After all, you're very good-looking. But I'm surprised you feel the same way about me.'

'So am I. You looked like a skinny kitten for the first month I knew you.' He eyed her. 'That's another new dress, isn't it?'

'It's a SAM one.'

'Isn't that the designer Bruce wants for the film?'

She saw his thoughts had reverted to his work, and was dismayed.

'We were talking about *us*,' she said.

'I don't want to pursue the subject.' He picked up his pen. 'Did you come in here for anything particular?'

'Only to see how you were.'

'I'm fine, thank you. When you go downstairs, ask Arthur to bring me up a cold drink. The pitcher's empty.'

Seeing the words as a dismissal, Samantha went down to the kitchen. It was empty and the station wagon was no longer by the gate, which meant that Arthur had gone shopping and she would be able to look after Bart herself. Refilling the pitcher from the huge jug of fresh juice in the refrigerator, she took it up to him, ignoring his obvious displeasure at the sight of her.

'I know I'm not wanted here, but Arthur's out and it was a choice between you having me to bring you a drink or remaining thirsty.'

Bart had the grace to look ashamed, almost as if he remembered that she had sat with him throughout the night.

'Now you're here,' he said, 'perhaps you would like to read what I've written so far?'

'Me?'

Samantha was amazed, for he had once said he did not like the lay public to read his work until it was finished.

'I'm interested in your opinion,' he went on, almost as if he knew what she was thinking. 'Diana's a young woman of your own age and you can tell me what you think of her.'

'I thought Linda had already done that?'

'Linda sees Diana from an actress's point of view.'

Samantha took the pile of manuscript and settled herself in the chair beside the bed. Bart went on writing, muttering aloud occasionally as he tested a bit of dialogue, but Samantha barely heard him. She was so immersed in the story that everything else faded from her mind.

She had always enjoyed Bart's novels, but this was the first time she had read a script of his, and she marvelled at how rounded his characters were. Graham and Diana were so alive that she would have known them immediately if they had walked into the room. Yet something was missing. At first she was not sure what it was. Then she began to see what Linda had meant when she complained that Diana was an unlovable woman.

Lost in thought, Samantha dropped the manuscript on her lap. Bart looked across at her, his expression quizzical as he waited for her comments.

'Either you're struck dumb with admiration or you dislike it so much you don't know how to tell me diplomatically,' he said.

'I wasn't trying to be diplomatic,' she confessed. 'I was wondering how to explain what I feel. Most of your characters are so alive. . . .'

'But?'

'But Diana's stereotyped.'

'Really?' Bart's voice was cool. 'I thought you liked my books?'

'I do. But this is a screen play, so there's no narrative to soften the edges of a character. One sees the stark outlines.'

'It's difficult to judge a script if you aren't used to reading one,' Bart said curtly, and held out his hand for it. 'I'm sorry you don't like Diana.'

He lowered his head and started to write again, making it clear he wanted to close the conversation.

'It's not only Diana,' Samantha continued boldly. 'Now I think about it, it's Graham too. He's as stereotyped as she is. He sees things in one way and closes his mind to any point of view other than his own. There are many occasions when Diana says things to him that he refuses to understand, yet he's continually complaining that she never understands *him*.'

'She doesn't,' Bart said. 'She's too selfish to think of anyone except herself.'

'Then she and Graham are well matched. He's a frightened little boy who says he wants to love a compassionate woman, yet if he met one, he'd run a mile from her.'

'Is that so?' Bart's voice was colder than she had known

it. 'I don't happen to see him that way.'

'Because you're too close to him. But I'm seeing him for the first time, and to me he's a man who's scared stiff of commitment.'

'Rubbish!'

'It isn't rubbish. I can't make you see my point of view, but I assure you a lot of people will see the film and think of Graham the same way that I do.'

Samantha heard her voice ringing in her ears, as if it was somebody else talking, and suddenly knew she wasn't describing Graham, but Bart.

'Graham is you,' she accused. 'You've put your own thoughts about women into Graham's mouth. That's why Diana is such a caricature, why all your women are cold, selfish bitches. In that way they can never be a threat to a man, because no man of intelligence would want them on a permanent basis!'

Samantha stopped speaking as she saw derision on Bart's face. She regretted her blunt words, knowing that what she felt for Bart had coloured her criticism of the play.

'I suppose you think Graham should love a selfish gold-digger like Diana?' he demanded.

'He does love her,' Samantha stated. 'That's why the script doesn't make sense. What comes through to me is that Graham doesn't leave Diana because he despises her, but because he's afraid of her. He knows that despite all her faults, she's the only woman he wants.'

'Wanting a woman doesn't mean loving a woman,' Bart said harshly. 'You still have romantic notions about sex.'

Samantha refused to rise to his bait. 'You asked for my opinion about the screen play, and I'm giving it to you. All your heroes are twisted in their relationships with women. It's the one continuing theme that runs through everything you write.'

'The critics don't appear to agree with you.'

'Because the critics only read your novels. This is the

first film script you've done yourself, and you've laid your characters bare.'

'What do you think Graham should do, then?' Bart asked sarcastically. 'Accept Diana for what she is and tie himself to a woman he knows to be a cheat?'

'But he's known what she is all along. That's why he had no compunction in using her. He only starts to hate when he realises he's fallen in love with her.'

'Then what in hell do you want him to do?' Bart repeated viciously.

'I think he should take a hard look at *himself*.' Samantha stared fixedly into Bart's face. 'Look into Graham's future, and tell me what you see for him. All I can see are other women like Diana, some a little more subtle, others even more obvious.'

'Are you trying to tell me a man only finds what he wants to find?'

'Yes. Some people would call it making their own destiny.'

'I'd call it a load of rubbish,' he said curtly. 'You'd better stick to housekeeping, Samantha. You're pretty lousy at it, but you're a damned sight better than you are as a critic.'

Distressed, Samantha moved nearer to the bed. How would she react if an outsider walked into her office, looked at her designs and then criticised them? She would be furious, feeling she had learned her craft the hard way and that no one, unless they had achieved equal success in the same field, had the right to stand in judgment upon her.

Yet such an attitude was wrong, for it was often the innocent eye that saw the truth. 'Suffer the little children. . . .' But Bart would suffer no one's opinion and, because she had been honest with him, she had probably destroyed their already tenuous relationship.

'I'm sorry, Bart, I had no right to criticise the script. Bruce likes it and it's his opinion that matters.'

'Don't apologise for being honest, Samantha.' Bart did

not look up. 'I should have known that no woman can resist becoming personal when she's given the opportunity. It's one of your sex's least likeable characteristics.'

'And denigrating women is one of *your* sex's least likeable characteristics!'

He did not say anything and Samantha turned sharply to the door. Annoyance made her forget her injured ankle and she put her weight on it. An agonising pain shot up into her calf and she cried out and stumbled.

Instantly Bart lunged forward and caught hold of her, pulling her back against the bed to prevent her from falling. She staggered and collapsed down beside him. For an instant she lay motionless, then as she tried to get up, Bart's other arm came over her and he pulled her further on to the bed.

His breath was warm on her face, his eyes so close that they blurred, going completely out of focus as he lowered his head until their lips touched.

The anger she had expected to feel in his kiss was not there. Instead there was warmth and a passion which deepened as the kiss continued. He moved his hands from her shoulders and clasped them round her waist to draw her closer to him. There was only a cotton counterpane between them and she could clearly feel the contours of his thighs and sinewy legs. Then he moved and the whole of his body covered hers.

'How quick you are to criticise,' he murmured huskily. 'Like all young people you believe everything can be talked away; that if you bring something into the open you can make it disappear. But emotions aren't like that. Many of them are too deep to reach the surface. And even if they do rise on occasion, they usually sink again and go deeper still.'

'*Yours* aren't deep, she said, abandoning all pretence that she had not been talking on a personal level. 'All the love interest in your books and in this play are based on your parents' marriage, and what you think of your mother.'

She felt his body tense, though he did not move back from her.

'You're being very blunt, little Samantha.'

'What's the point of pretending? You did ask for my opinion, didn't you? I know you're angry with me, so I might as well be hanged for a sheep as a lamb.'

'Go on,' he said softly. 'Steal the whole sheep.'

She hesitated, wanting him to make love to her, yet knowing that despite his physical closeness to her, his mind was still miles away emotionally.

'You won't allow yourself to live your *own* life,' she said finally. 'You've built it on your father's ruins. But you've got your own foundations, Bart, and I don't believe they're as shaky as you think.'

'You should have me on a couch, instead of a bed,' he drawled.

'I don't need to have you anywhere to analyse you. You're easy to read. You're running away from love because you're as frightened and selfish as Graham.'

'How flattering you are! Frightened and selfish, am I? Let's see if we can find some other adjectives to describe me.'

He began to rain kisses down the side of her face, then pushed aside the top of her blouse to kiss the more delicate skin at the base of her throat.

'Such a tiny girl,' he crooned. 'No one would suspect you have a viper's tongue inside that pink little mouth. Give it to me, Samantha. Let me feel its softness instead of its sting.'

She knew she should refuse him, but his closeness made her powerless to resist. He pressed himself harder upon her and cupped her chin, forcing her head round to look at him.

'Give it to me,' he ordered.

'You can't make me.'

'Can't I?'

His mouth fastened on hers, its pressure so hard that it forced her lips apart. She was sure women did not often resist him. Even if he had not been famous and successful they would have found his virility too overpowering to ignore.

Feeling him close, hearing his quick breathing and the slow thudding of his heart, Samantha felt him to be a lonely boy rather than an all-conquering man, and it was the little boy in him which made her put her arms round his shoulders and run her hands down his back. His spine was firm beneath the thin silk of his pyjama jacket and, as he felt the movement of her fingers, he shivered convulsively and pressed her tighter against him.

A deep wave of desire engulfed her, playing havoc with her strength of mind. She could no longer fight her longing to be taken by him. She wanted him and she was not ashamed to admit it. Moving her hands lower down his back, she waited for him to make their fusion complete.

'Darling,' he whispered, and momentarily lifted his mouth from hers, half opening his eyes to see her grey ones glazed with passion.

'Darling,' he said again. 'I want you.'

'I know,' she whispered, and slipped her hand inside his pyjama jacket to caress his bronze skin.

He moaned and roughly pulled at her sweater, then moved his hand beneath it. She was not wearing a bra and his fingers instantly found her breasts and cupped them She trembled and clutched at him with shaking hands.

'Bart,' she whispered, 'love me, love me.'

'Love,' he echoed thickly, and then his voice broke. 'No—no, I can't!' With a lurch he pushed her away from him, sending her half-way across the bed. 'No,' he repeated in a strangled voice. 'Don't ask the impossible. I'll make love to you—God knows it's what I want to do more than anything else—but I can't love you. I won't!'

Samantha listened to him unbelievingly, trying to resist

what he said, yet feeling the words enter her—the way she had wanted him to do—and corrode her with their bitterness.

Bart lay flat against the pillows, staring up at the ceiling yet not seeing it. Samantha looked at his profile, loving yet hating the strength of character which it revealed.

'You don't mean it,' she whispered, and moved across the bed towards him, wanting to lie close to him, to nestle against the curve of his shoulder. In that moment he was the father she had lost, the protector she needed.

'I do mean it,' he said violently. 'I don't want to love anyone. I enjoy my life the way it is—taking when I want to take, discarding when I want to discard. It's the way I planned my life and I won't let a five-foot-nothing scrap of a girl seduce me into changing it.'

'*I* wasn't the seducer,' she said flatly.

There was a pause, then a sigh came from the depths of him. 'You're right, little one. It was my fault. But you're a tantalising witch and I wanted you badly. I still do—as you can see. But I'm not going to do anything about it. The last thing I need is an affair that will make me feel guilty.'

Silently Samantha rose, straightened her sweater and smoothed her hair.

'How virginal you look.' His voice was soft and she half turned and looked at him over her shoulder.

'I am,' she said. 'I don't expect you to believe me after the display I just gave, but——'

'I know you are.' There was a teasing note in his voice. 'You touched me as if you were touching fire!' She went scarlet and he gave another sigh. 'I've never been one to rate innocence all that highly, but on you it looks good. That's why I won't be the one to take it away.'

'I'll have to lose it some time.'

'But not with me. Find yourself a young man who believes in your kind of love.'

'Maybe *you* could learn to believe it.'

'How can I believe in something I despise?'

She could not think of any reply to this and she went out. For a brief instant she stood in the corridor, then she loosened her fingers from the handle and walked away, knowing she was leaving her happiness behind her.

CHAPTER THIRTEEN

SAMANTHA did not visit Bart again that evening nor the following day. The weather was exceptionally hot and she stayed in the front garden, where Bart could not see her from his bedroom window. Dr Baxter called round to see him and pronounced him much better, though he advised him to stay in bed for another few days.

Again and again Samantha re-lived the scene in Bart's room. He persisted in seeing her as a child despite his own desire for her, and she realised that this was a defence mechanism. If he pretended she was not yet a woman, he could tell himself he was not running away from her because he was afraid of falling in love with her.

Poor Bart! Even though she despised his self-deception, she pitied him for the unhappy childhood that had marked itself indelibly on his behaviour.

Her own childhood, in contrast, had been placid. Her father had died when she was in her late teens and four years ago her mother had remarried and gone to live in New Zealand. Samantha had flown out to see her once and, last year, had sent her a ticket to come and spend a month in England. It was odd that she had never considered staying with her mother when she herself became ill, and she supposed it was because she had wanted to get away from people who knew her.

Idly Samantha allowed herself to think of the work that lay ahead of her. The cruise collection she had been asked to design for a big American store had also included an invitation for her to visit New York when the collection was presented, and she toyed with the idea of going. She might even fly out to Hollywood and visit some of the stars for whom she had designed clothes, and who had so often begged her to stay with them.

Thinking of Hollywood reminded Samantha that Bruce Dorland wanted SAM to design the clothes for Bart's film. It was silly of her to continue with her deception. It was time she told Bart her true identity.

She rose from her deckchair and walked across the grass. Before she could reach the front door, it opened and Bart came out. He wore a pale grey suit with a white shirt and a dark grey tie. His hair was smoothly brushed and he could have been a city banker. Samantha had never seen him like this and she stared at him as if she was meeting a stranger.

'Shouldn't you still be in bed?' she asked.

'I haven't got a temperature.'

'Why are you dressed like that?'

'I'm going back to London.'

'But I ... I thought you wanted to stay here to finish you script?'

'It's nearly done.'

'Are you running away from me?'

Bart was silent, then almost when she had given up expecting him to answer, he inclined his head.

'You could put it that way. Yes.' His voice grew stronger. 'Yes, I am.'

'I suppose I should feel pleased with myself,' she shrugged

'Do you?'

'Not particularly. I feel sad—for *you*.'

'Spare me your sympathy,' he said abruptly. 'I'm doing what I want to do. You've got under my skin, and I'm cutting you out. I've always regarded women as a necessary evil, but they're only necessary to me from time to time. Unfortunately you wanted to make something permanent of it, and I'm not prepared for that. I have to remain free.'

Samantha knew it was pointless to argue with him. Besides, if she went on standing here she would burst into tears, and that would convince him even more strongly that he was doing the right thing to leave her.

'Goodbye, Bart,' she said in a thin voice and, head high, walked past him.

Samantha remained in her bedroom until she heard his car drive away. A few minutes later she went downstairs and was surprised to hear a noise coming from the kitchen. Arthur was by the gas stove, taking a cake from the oven.

Dumbfounded, Samantha gazed at him. 'I thought you'd left for London?'

'Mr Jackson can leave at a moment's notice, miss, but I can't. I have to clean the kitchen first.'

'It's perfectly clean,' she said, smiling broadly. Then suddenly she burst into tears. 'Oh, Arthur,' she sobbed, 'I'm so miserable I wish I were dead!'

Collapsing on to a chair, she cried the way she had cried as a child, with deep sobs that shook her body. Arthur made little clucking sounds but left her to her misery. He iced the cake and then made a pot of tea. Gradually Samantha's sobs subsided and she hiccuped a few times and wiped her eyes.

'You know I love Mr Jackson, don't you?'

'Yes, miss.'

'I bet you've heard a few women say that?'

'You're the only one I've believed.'

'Really?' she hiccuped.

'Truly, miss. You love him for what he is.'

'I ought to hate him for what he is.' Tears started into her eyes again. 'But I can't. He's such an unhappy man, Arthur, and he doesn't even know it.'

'He hasn't been unhappy so far,' Arthur said somewhat grimly. 'But I've a feeling he's going to be. You're the first female who's made him run away.'

'I'm afraid I don't see that as a good sign,' she said dejectedly.

'I'm not sure how to see it, miss,' Arthur admitted. 'I'm

just giving you the facts and letting you work them out for yourself.'

'There's nothing to work out, Arthur. Mr Jackson loves his freedom more than he loves me.' Samantha sipped her tea. 'I suppose you'll be leaving tomorrow?'

'Yes, miss. Though I don't like the thought of you being here by yourself.'

'I'll—I'll probably have a friend to stay with me.'

He looked relieved. 'Would you like me to go into Penzance and do some shopping for you? I've got the car and it'll be easy for me to stock up the larder.'

The thought of food nauseated her, but she knew that if she did not eat she would get ill again.

'That's a good idea. I'll come in with you.'

Half an hour later they set off for Penzance. With a disregard for money, Samantha bought every delectable food she saw and then nipped into the Post Office—on the pretext of getting some stamps—in order to send a telegram to Mrs Vivien asking her to return at once.

Arriving back at the cottage, Arthur grilled a fresh lobster they had bought in Penzance, smothered it in Cornish butter and served it with salad and a bottle of chilled Chablis. Samantha was usually a sparing drinker, but tonight she downed three glasses, thinking this was the best way to help her to sleep, yet knowing that no alcoholic haze could ever blur her memory of Bart.

In the morning Arthur departed, stiff-lipped and formal with his farewells, but obviously moved.

'It's been a pleasure knowing you, miss. I hope we'll meet again one day.'

'I doubt it, Arthur.' Samantha longed to give him her address, but knew if she saw him it would remind her of a man she was determined to forget.

When Arthur had driven away, the house seemed terribly quiet and Samantha could not bear to remain indoors. She wandered down to the beach and looked at the sparkling ocean and a couple of boats whose white sails broke the

line of the horizon. Would Bart return to Monte Carlo or
would he stay in London to supervise the making of his
picture? She wished she had asked Bruce more about it,
and then wondered if he had contacted her office. She
longed to ring Carol to find out, but decided not to do so
until her holiday ended in four weeks' time.

Samantha did not return home until the golden sun had
turned to orange and was sinking in the western sky. As
soon as she reached Gable Cottage she realised Mrs Vivien
was back. The radio was playing in the kitchen and Campbell was barking excitedly. Samantha ran in to welcome
the housekeeper and saw that the puppy was gambolling
around the woman's feet.

'What a little love he is! You never told me they'd de-
livered him.' Mrs Vivien exclaimed, putting on the kettle
to make a pot of tea.

'It slipped my mind,' Samantha confessed. 'I'm afraid
we've also given him a name. He's called Campbell.'

'Isn't that after a general?'

Samantha laughed. 'It's after a soup! As there are so
many varieties in his breeding, I was going to call him
Heinz—but someone else suggested another brand called
Campbells.'

Hearing his name, the puppy yelped excitedly and received a piece of cake which he quickly gobbled up.

Compared with the efficient and quick-footed Arthur,
Mrs Vivien seemed extremely plodding, but Samantha had
to admit that in her depressed mood, she was unlikely to
find anyone congenial company.

The days passed slowly. Samantha did a fair amount of
painting. She made several studies of the cottage, and a
sketch of Mrs Vivien which so delighted the woman that
she said she would have it framed.

August gave way to September and the good weather
broke, forcing Samantha to stay indoors except for an
occasional brisk walk in the rain. Amazingly she was sleep-

ing and eating well, although Bart was still as clearly etched in her mind as if she had seen him yesterday.

She was relieved she could think of him without pain, but knew it was only because she had not yet accepted the fact that he had walked out of her life and would never return. Each time she went out, she came back to the cottage expecting to see his red Mercedes parked outside the gate. Even when she was indoors and heard the sound of a high-powered engine approaching, she rushed to the window.

Finally only a week remained of her three months' enforced holiday, but Samantha knew she could not stand another day at Gable Cottage. She must return to London immediately.

'It was wonderful having you here to look after the house when I was ill,' Mrs Vivien said tearfully, when Samantha announced she was leaving. 'I hope you'll come down again with Miss Carol?'

Samantha nodded, but doubted if she would visit the cottage again; it held too many painful memories.

She drove to her house in Chelsea, changed into an elegant town dress and then took a taxi to Margaret Street. She had not warned anyone she was returning, and Carol greeted her with delighted astonishment.

'I didn't expect you back till the end of the month. You look great! Almost as good as new.'

'Almost?' queried Samantha.

'There are shadows under your eyes.'

'The journey was tiring,' Samantha lied, and went into her office. Carol followed, closing the door behind her.

'I'm glad you're back, Samantha. I was thinking of ringing you.'

'What's the panic?'

'No panic—on the contrary, it's good news.' Carol perched on the edge of the desk as Samantha settled behind it. 'How would you fancy doing the clothes for the new Jackson Bart film? It's a four-million-pound epic and you'd have a huge budget to play with. I had Bruce Dorland, the producer, on the telephone to me this morning, asking if he could see you.'

'No.'

'I told him you wouldn't be back for a week, but. . . .' Carol's voice trailed off. 'Did you say "no"?'

'Yes. I don't want to do the film.'

'Why?' Carol demanded and, in the face of Samantha's silence, said crossly: 'You can't just say no and then refuse to discuss it.'

Samantha knew that as Carol's employer she could do exactly that, but because Carol was her friend, she felt obligated to explain the situation.

'I met Bart Jackson in Cornwall. That's his real name, by the way—he just reversed it for a pseudonym. Your aunt very kindly offered him the use of the cottage and he went down expecting to be there on his own. He also thought I was the housekeeper.'

Carol's mouth fell open, and she listened in amazement as Samantha described what had happened; telling the story factually and not lying about her feelings nor the way Bart had reacted to them.

'He loves his freedom,' she concluded, 'and he ran away rather than let anyone take it away from him.'

'But you aren't "anyone". The man's crazy—mad!'

'Because he refused to be ruled by his emotions?' Samantha asked drily. 'Maybe I'm the one who's mad for thinking the heart could rule the head.'

She began to look through the letters stacked on her desk. The pile was surprisingly small and Carol, knowing Samantha did not wish to talk about Bart Jackson, explained that most of the correspondence had been dealt with.

'One or two clients wanted to contact you personally and became stroppy when I wouldn't tell them where you were. But the majority of them have been quite happy to deal with me—though they won't be once they realise you're back. Perhaps we shouldn't broadcast it around for a while?'

'On the contrary,' Samantha said grimly. 'The more I have to do the better. I want something to stop me thinking of myself.'

'I hope that doesn't mean you'll work your way into another collapse?'

'I'll collapse if I *don't* work. It's all I've got left.'

Quickly Samantha took up the reins of her business again, but one part of her mind remained completely detached. In this part was enshrined the memory of Bart. She had only to close her eyes to see his face; only to be alone in a silent room to hear his voice.

September gave way to October and the leaves turned golden on the trees and fluttered to the ground, leaving twigs as bare as her own future. Despite the desolation within her, Samantha's cruise collection turned out to be a great success and once again she toyed with the idea of going to New York and Hollywood.

'I need some fun,' she explained to Carol, 'and I can't seem to find it here.'

'You're not a "fun" girl, and you won't find it anywhere.'

'Yes, I will. I've made up my mind.'

'You've made it up wrongly, then.' Carol sounded distressed. 'Look for another man who will give you what you really want.'

'I want fun,' came the stubborn reply.

'If you genuinely meant that, you'd go back to Bart.'

It was too true a comment for Samantha to deny. 'Sometimes I wish you didn't know me so well,' she grumbled.

'I haven't finished yet, either,' said Carol. 'If you won't go back to Bart Jackson, then for God's sake stop mooning over him.'

'Don't you think I'm trying?'

'Not hard enough.'

'What else do you suggest I do?'

'The first thing is to come down to the cottage with me. I have to go and see Mrs Vivien.'

'I couldn't go there yet.' Not ever, Samantha thought to herself, but knew better than to say so aloud.

'Okay,' Carol muttered. 'I'll let you get away with refusing this time, but on the next occasion I won't take no for an answer.'

On the Friday, Carol went alone to Cornwall, and returned to the office on Tuesday bursting with news.

'You'll never guess who was at the cottage last week,' she exclaimed. 'In fact, if I'd gone a day earlier, I would have met him.'

Samantha was silent.

'Well,' Carol demanded, 'don't you want to know?'

'It was Bart,' said Samantha.

'That's right. He expected to find you, and he had a fit when Mrs Vivien told him *she* was the housekeeper and that you were a friend of mine who'd been staying there for a holiday.'

Samantha moistened lips that were suddenly dry. 'Did she.... She didn't say who I was?'

'Luckily she still doesn't know. You never told her the truth. She said she had no idea where you lived and told him to contact me. She gave him this phone number.'

'Oh God!' Samantha recoiled from the telephone on the desk as if it might attack her. 'If he rings here you mustn't tell him where I am—or even who I am. Say I'm—say I'm a secretary and that I've left and gone to Canada.'

'Why Canada?'

'Australia, then,' Samantha said wildly. 'Make it anywhere except England.'

'Don't you want to see him?'

'Of course I want to see him. But I don't want a love affair with him,' she added bitterly. 'That's the only reason he went back to find me.'

'Maybe you *should* have an affair with him,' Carol stated.

'Why have you suddenly changed your tune? The other day, when I said I wanted some fun, you nearly blew your top. Yet now you're telling me to——'

'Because you love him.'

'All the more reason to keep out of his bed. If I let him ... if I.... No, I couldn't. It would shatter me when we broke up.'

'It might not break up.'

Samantha looked grim. 'I can imagine the number of girls who went into an affair with Bart hoping exactly the same thing.'

'But he feels differently about you. You said so yourself.'

'Not differently enough to marry me.' The slanting eyes narrowed. 'Until I fell for Bart, I never realised how old-fashioned I was. That's why I don't want to see him again. If I did, I might not be strong enough to resist him. That's why you must promise me never to tell him I'm here.'

'If that's the way you want it,' Carol shrugged. 'But I think it would be better for you to face him. It's like confronting the devil instead of running away!'

For the rest of the day Samantha was on tenterhooks. Every time the telephone rang she expected it to be Bart, and though she had left word with the switchboard that if anyone rang up asking for Miss Rose, they were to be connected to Carol, she still dared not pick up the telephone herself in case Bart was put through by mistake.

But Bart did not ring, though the next morning Bruce Dorland did.

Samantha's secretary buzzed her on the intercom, and Samantha asked Carol to come into the office and take the call, first telling her friend what to say.

'Are you absolutely sure you want to turn down the offer?' Carol asked in a final attempt to make Samantha change her mind. 'It would be fantastic publicity for you.'

'I don't need any more publicity. Take the call and put him off. Firmly.'

Airily Carol did as she was told, explaining to Bruce that her employer was far too busy at present to take on any more commitments, and would shortly be leaving for America for an indefinite period.

'I'm afraid it won't make any difference if you speak to her personally,' Carol told him when he showed no sign of accepting a turn down. 'But perhaps when you're producing another film, you could get in touch with us again.'

Samantha waved her arms wildly and her friend pulled a face at her and then managed to bring the conversation to a close.

'He was absolutely livid,' Carol said, swinging round to the desk. 'It's a pity Bart Jackson isn't so persistent. He hasn't rung me yet.'

'Perhaps his urge to find me cooled off by the time he returned to London.'

'Then he's——'

'Call for you on the outside line, Carol,' said Samantha's secretary, putting her head round the door. 'Do you want to take it in here?'

Carol nodded and picked up the telephone again. Her face changed colour as she listened and Samantha knew instantly that it was Bart. She wanted to run from the room, but her legs would not carry her, and she remained seated, shaking in every limb.

'Yes, Mr Jackson, Miss Rose did work here,' Carol was saying. 'But she left a few weeks ago. . . . She went to Australia, as a matter of fact, but I don't have her address. She promised to write to me as soon as she's settled, so if you tell me where I can contact you. . . .'

Carol wrote busily on a pad, said a terse goodbye and collapsed on to a chair beside the desk.

Samantha forced herself to remain quiet and pretended an interest in some drawings in front of her.

'What a man!' Carol said into the silence. 'Even through the telephone I could feel his charm. But I think I fobbed him off, so you've nothing to worry about.'

'Good.'

'He soundéd very regretful, though.'

'Because he missed out on a conquest. I shouldn't think many women run away from him.'

'He was the one who did the running away, remember?'

'I'm trying not to remember,' Samantha said. 'Maybe in a year or two I'll succeed.'

'And if you don't?'

'I'll satisfy myself with a loveless marriage! Now for God's sake let's change the subject and forget that men exist.'

CHAPTER FOURTEEN

DURING the next few days Samantha's desire to go to the States faded. It was cowardly to run away from Bart by crossing the Atlantic. If she concentrated on her work, she was as likely to forget him in London as in Hollywood.

Obviously Bart was still attracted to her. That was why he had returned to Cornwall. It would be easy to accept him on his own terms and have a casual affair, but she knew it would not work. The more she saw of him, the deeper her feelings would grow, making the pain unbearable when he finally left her.

She had a feeling he would contact Carol again, but when a week passed with no word from him, she began to relax.

Because of her long absence, there was a great deal of work to be cleared up on the administrative side, but after her enforced rest she found it difficult to get back into the rhythm of work. She had the energy to do so but found she lacked the inclination. It suddenly seemed to her that life was too short to spend so much time doing things one did not enjoy.

At a meeting with her accountant, Lloyd Thomas, Samantha took the plunge.

'If I can remain in charge of the designing, I'd be willing to sell out. But I'm fed up wasting so much of my time dealing with financial matters and staff problems.'

'There'll be no shortage of buyers,' Lloyd Thomas assured her. 'It's merely a question of choosing the company with whom you'd be most happy to work.'

'A British one,' she said. 'You know the price I want and you know I'm prepared to bargain.'

'You won't need to bargain. You're the biggest success

since sliced bread, and you can name your own price.' He smiled. 'What will you do with all the money?'

'Put it in the bank and forget it.'

When the accountant had gone, Samantha closed her eyes and thought of her future. Free of administrative responsibility, she would be able to work and live where she liked, only returning to London to supervise the collections. It would be the ideal life. She thanked the fates that had given her influenza and forced her to relax and take stock of herself.

The intercom buzzed on her desk and she sat up sharply. 'What is it?'

'Carol's on her way to see you, Miss Gardner. It's urgent,' her secretary said.

The intercom went dead and Samantha half rose, stopping as the door opened and Carol rushed in.

'He's outside!' her friend said in a whisper.

Samantha had no need to ask to whom the 'he' referred. Yet she felt no fear or excitement.

'Did you tell him Miss Rose had gone to Australia?' she asked.

'Yes, but he still won't leave.'

'Why?'

'Because I'm not such a fool as you think.' With these words, Bart strode into the room.

I'd forgotten how tall he was, Samantha thought, and watched helplessly as he stopped within a pace of her. His eyes were blazing and his mouth was set in a narrow line.

'I don't like being given the run-around, Samantha. I knew damned well you hadn't gone to Australia.'

'Then why didn't you take the hint and realise I don't want to see you?'

Tactfully Carol left the room, and Samantha moved to the window, putting the width of the designing board between herself and Bart.

'Why did you want to see me again?' Samantha asked coldly.

'Because I love you. I haven't been able to get you out of my mind. I know that living with you won't be easy, and there'll be times when you'll drive me to distraction with your illogicality and bossiness, but I also know I can't live without you.'

'Then living with me is the lesser of two evils?'

'That's right,' Bart smiled. 'But *I'm* not easy to live with either. Still, I think we'll be a damned sight happier together than we are apart.'

'And you come here expecting me to agree with you?'

'Don't you?' He moved towards her. 'Don't pretend, Samantha. You can't forget me any more than I can forget you.'

Samantha's temper was rising. How dared he callously run away from her and then expect her to fall into his arms the moment it suited him?

'I'm not pretending to be indifferent to you, Bart, but I don't want you,' she said flatly. 'What I felt for you was a summer madness.'

'Don't talk like a cheap romance!'

'Then don't behave like a cheap Casanova!'

His eyes blazed. 'Is that what you think I am?'

She hesitated, then shrugged. 'Not quite. I'll give you a little more credit than that. But I don't want to get involved with you again.'

'You haven't even begun to get involved with me,' he said roughly. 'If I'd let you seduce me when I was ill, and we'd made love, you wouldn't find it so easy to turn me down now.'

'You conceited swine!' Samantha glared at him. 'I suppose you think physical love is all-important?'

'It's one of the most important.'

'But without other things it's meaningless. And it's all those other things, which you don't have.'

'Such as?' Bart demanded.

'What's the use of my telling you? You wouldn't understand. You see love differently from the way I do.'

'Naturally. I'm a man.'

For a few seconds neither spoke. Bart looked perplexed, as if he were at a loss for words, and Samantha decided to break the silence.

'I'm not interested in having a love affair with you, Bart. So stop wasting your time with me.'

'I'm not wasting it. I want to marry you. I want you to belong to me.'

She was startled. '*Marry* me?'

'That's right.'

'And to whom would *you* belong?'

His eyebrows shot up, as if it was a question he had not considered.

'You see,' Samantha said gently. 'It wouldn't work. If I belonged to you, then you would have to belong to me. Marriage should be an equal partnership.'

'What makes you think ours wouldn't be? Can't you understand what I'm saying to you? I need you, Samantha, I need you so badly that I couldn't stay in Monte Carlo without you. I couldn't work; your face kept staring at me from the typewriter. Each time I looked at the bloody keys I saw your eyes. You haunted my days and you turned my sleep into a nightmare of longing. You *have* to marry me,' he said earnestly, his deep voice so low that it was practicaally inaudible. 'Come away with me now. I've got a licence and we can be married today.'

The intercom buzzed on Samantha's desk and her secretary's voice was loud in the room.

'Mr Marburg is calling you from New York, Miss Gardner. I know you're busy, but you did say you wished to speak to him.'

'I do,' Samantha replied, ignoring Bart. 'Put him through.'

Mr Marburg's voice came on the line, as clear as if he were in the room. He was a manufacturer for whom she had recently designed a range of household linen, and he was eager to have her do more work for him.

'I just wanted to tell you that the designs you sent us are great,' he extolled. 'If you could translate some of them into patterns for china, I have a Japanese manufacturer ready to sign on the dotted line.'

'I'll think about it,' she hedged. 'I'm in the middle of negotiating the sale of my business, and after the end of the month I might not be a free agent.'

'You aren't giving up, are you?' he asked, horrified.

'Only so that I can spend all my time on design instead of administration.'

'Then I'm all for it,' he said enthusiastically. 'It's a wise move, Samantha. But if I can't negotiate with you, to whom do I talk?'

'I'll let you know as soon as possible,' she replied, unwilling to give away too much information until the contracts had been signed. 'But you won't have anything to worry about, Mr Marburg. I'll still work for you.'

Samantha put down the telephone and looked at Bart. It was only as she saw his amazed expression that she realised that until this moment he had not known her true identity.

'A rose by any other name,' he said slowly. 'So you're the famous SAM? The laugh's really on me, isn't it?'

'I'm still the girl you fell in love with,' she reminded him. 'But when you came in just now and said you knew the truth, I thought you really did.'

'Not the whole truth. No wonder you turned me down!'

She did not follow his reasoning and her puzzlement showed it.

'Why should you give up a successful career and follow a man around?' he explained.

'Is that what I'd have had to do?' Samantha asked sweetly. 'I thought you wanted a wife. I hadn't realised you meant a slave.'

'Marriage is a form of willing slavery,' he said.

'Not the sort of marriage I want. It's companionship;

a sharing of ideas and thoughts as well as passions. It's giving as well as taking—though I don't expect you to understand that.'

She remained behind her desk and vowed that if Bart came towards her, she would sidestep him and run from the room. She had had more than she could take of his nearness, and she knew that if he touched her she would be unable to withstand him. Already she was feeling faint and the room was beginning to swim.

'Please go, Bart.' She sat down on her chair, keeping the movement slow so that he should not guess she was at the end of her tether. 'We have nothing more to say to each other.'

'How you must have laughed when I made you buy that blue frilly dress,' he went on, as if he had not heard a word she had said. 'What a joke it was for you when you cobbled that button on to my shirt, and when you pretended to be so helpless around the house!'

'I am helpless around the house,' she replied. 'Though I admit I was making fun of you when I sewed the button on your shirt.'

She stared at the intercom, willing it to ring again and put an end to this conversation. But it remained obstinately silent and she dug her nails into the palms of her hands, concentrating on the pain she was causing herself in the hope that it would stop her from being swayed by his presence.

'We'd never be happy together, Bart. Our personalities are too different. Our marriage would be one row after another.'

'I don't agree with you. I only get bad-tempered when I'm bored, and you'd never bore me.'

'But you'd bore *me*,' she said cruelly, wanting to pay him back for all the hurt he had caused her. 'Find another woman with whom you can play the big, sexy author. I'm opting out.'

'Your love for me didn't last long, did it?' His voice was so slurred that, had she not known better, she would have believed him to be drunk.

'People change,' she said lightly.

'Yet you refuse to accept that I have?'

'Because I know you haven't,'

'Then I won't waste my time trying to convince you that you're wrong.'

As he spoke, he strode to the door and went out, leaving her staring after him and wondering if she were crazy to have thrown away her chance of happiness.

'It wouldn't have worked,' she told Carol, when her friend came in and found her sitting slumped over her desk. 'He only asked me to marry him because he knew he couldn't get me into bed any other way. But once I was his wife, he'd start hating me for taking away his freedom.'

'You could be right,' Carol said. 'I don't know him well enough to agree or disagree with you. All I know is that it seems ludicrous for you to turn him down when you still love him.'

Many times in the weeks that followed, Samantha thought the same as Carol. But each time her hand hovered on the telephone to call Bart's publishers and ask for his telephone number, she resisted it for the weakness that it was, knowing that what he felt for her was nothing more than physical attraction and that when this ebbed, as physical attraction inevitably did, there would be no genuine love to replace it.

'So what's wrong with physical attraction?' Carol demanded one evening in late October when she was having dinner at Samantha's pretty Chelsea house.

That morning, Samantha had completed the sale of her business to a British textile giant, receiving even more money than her accountant had first promised her, as well as the complete freedom to design when, where and what she wanted.

'You shouldn't be celebrating with me,' Carol continued.

'You should be with that great hunk of manhood you still love. You wouldn't catch me turning him down if I got the chance.'

'How long would our marriage have lasted?' Samantha questioned.

'Until you turned into a wrinkled old hag,' Carol teased. 'Honestly, Sam, you're a good-looking girl, but if it were just the physical side which appealed to him, I bet he's been out with far more stunning-looking birds.'

'He liked the fact that I fought with him,' Samantha admitted. 'But once he possessed me, he'd get tired of me.'

'Would you get tired of him?'

'Of course not. But I happen to love him.'

'Then why do you talk as if you hate him?'

'Don't be silly!'

'I'm not being silly,' said Carol. 'You do hate him. You hate him because he isn't dependent on you, and because he has a mind of his own. If you'd had any sense you'd have become his wife and let nature take its course. It's my belief that once he started living with you, he'd wonder how he ever managed to live without you.'

'I think the exact opposite. I believe he'd grow to resent me; that he'd chafe at the ties and find it hard to be faithful.'

'After the way he saw his mother behave? You've got to be kidding! Once Bart Jackson decided on marriage, he'd work at it for the rest of his life. You made a mistake, Samantha, and it's time you put it right.'

Long after Carol had gone, Samantha considered everything her friend had said, and knew that if Bart came to her now and asked her to be his wife, she would not turn him down.

Common sense told her to contact him, but pride made it impossible, and she fought with herself for a week before she finally succumbed.

Yet having made up her mind to call Bart, it was difficult to actually do so, for his number in Monte Carlo was ex-directory and neither his agent nor publisher would disclose it. Firmly they told her to write to Mr Jackson, promising that any letter would be forwarded.

Reluctant to face such a delay, she telephoned Bruce at Elstree studios, where Bart's film was being made.

'There must be something in telepathy, after all,' Bruce announced after greeting her warmly. 'I have a note on my pad to call you this morning.'

'Any special reason?' she asked, trying to sound casual, but desperately afraid he was going to tell her Bart had married someone else.

'Only to plead with you to change your mind and design the dresses for the film,' said Bruce. 'Which reminds me, this is the first time I've spoken to you since Bart told me *you* are SAM. I suppose you know I spoke to your assistant and practically went down on my knees trying to make an appointment to see you—which she refused?'

'I'm sorry,' Samantha said contritely. 'But at that time I was—I was very busy and—and I didn't want to see anyone who reminded me of Bart.'

'You're making me highly curious,' Bruce told her. 'I'd like to hear the whole story. You wouldn't be free to have dinner with me tonight, would you?'

'Is it so important for you to hear the story?' she asked lightly, knowing she was talking for talking's sake, but only because she found herself unable to ask him bluntly for Bart's telephone number.

'Everything about you is important to me,' Bruce replied. 'So give me your address and I'll pick you up at eight—if not tonight, then tomorrow or the night after.'

'You're very persistent,' she teased, but agreed to see him that evening. She had waited so long before contacting Bart that another day would not matter. Anyway, Bruce was bound to talk about him tonight, and what she learned would either harden her resolve to see him or destroy it completely.

Samantha was waiting for Bruce long before he was

due to arrive. She wore one of her own designed dresses and looked infinitely fragile in black, a colour which matched her sombre mood.

The sight of Bruce's beaming face did much to cheer her up. He dumped an enormous bunch of long-stemmed red roses into her arms and kissed her.

'Quite a transition from Mrs Barclay's housekeeper,' he commented, glancing round the elegant lounge, with its modern Italian furniture and original Hockneys on the walls. 'The only person who wasn't surprised by the truth was Arthur. He said he knew all along you weren't a housekeeper.'

'Only because I was such a dreadful one.' Samantha grinned, pouring Bruce a whisky. 'Let's drink a toast to him.'

'To Arthur,' said Bruce, and they solemnly drank.

'And now let's drink a toast to you,' Bruce said, 'and to the hope that you'll have a change of heart and design the dresses for the film.'

'I heard you've already got Manuel Lopez?'

'He doesn't have your deft touch.'

'But surely half the film's already been shot?'

'Not quite half,' Bruce shrugged. 'And we haven't touched any of the big scenes yet. Come on, Samantha, say yes. I've been reading about the wonderful deal you've just made, so I know you don't need the money, but——'

'I don't,' she agreed.

'But you do like to design clothes,' he went on, 'and this film would be a real challenge for you.'

'Don't press it,' said Samantha, turning away to pick up a fur jacket. 'Where are we having dinner?'

'At Lothario's.' Bruce named the newest restaurant in town, and then casually began to talk of other things.

He kept up a flow of light conversation throughout the main part of the meal, and it was only when they were sipping coffee that he referred to Bart.

'It's six weeks since I've seen him.' Bruce's look was keen.

'Just after he was in London and saw you, in fact.'

Samantha twirled her spoon in her cup, disregarding the fact that she never took sugar. There was something in Bruce's voice that told her he knew Bart had asked her to marry him, and though this gave her the perfect excuse to ask Bart's telephone number, she still found herself holding back.

'Why did you turn him down?' Bruce asked bluntly. 'I'd have taken a bet you were keen on him.'

'Then you'd have lost your bet. Not every girl who meets Bart falls in love with him.'

'Enough of them do for me to question your motives for saying no,' Bruce answered. 'You look like a million pounds, Samantha—and you're probably worth it now, but you've got shadows under your eyes and you look as if a puff of wind could blow you away.'

'I've been working hard. Very hard,' she repeated, seeing his sceptical look.

'That makes two of you,' he said.

'Two?'

'You and Bart. As I said, I haven't seen him since he went back to Monte Carlo and locked himself away from the world. I've spoken to him on the telephone when I've wanted a few script changes, but he refuses to come over.'

'If you're trying to tell me it's because he's nursing a broken heart,' Samantha said, 'then forget it. Bart always shuts himself away from everyone when he's working on a new book.' She set down her coffee spoon. 'I'm glad that my refusing his proposal hasn't affected his writing.'

'You're a tough nut, Samantha.'

'That makes two of us.'

'Two?'

'Bart and myself,' she said sweetly, and was now quite sure she was not going to ask for his telephone number.

Hearing Bart was working on a new book had changed her mind. If he had loved her as deeply as he professed, her refusal to marry him would have made him too upset to immerse himself so quickly in his work. She was right when she had called him a hard man. All she had done was to underestimate the hardness. Well, if he could work, so could she.

'Let me read the film script,' she said. 'I only read a bit of it in Cornwall. If I like it, I may do the designs.'

'Come down to the studio first,' Bruce suggested. 'Make it tomorrow, if you're free. I'll send a car for you.'

She knew he was desperate to have her make a decision and could not help being flattered.

'Wouldn't it be better to wait until I've read the script?' she asked.

'You can do that at the studio, and you'll also be able to see the sets and get a feel about the whole thing.'

'Very well,' she said. 'But don't bother sending a car for me; I'll drive myself down.'

Preparing for bed that night, Samantha chided herself for being a fool. If she did not wish to see Bart again she had no business involving herself in anything that would keep him in her mind. Yet she wanted him back, and the only reason she stayed away from him was the uncertainty of their future together.

Yet she had promised Bruce she would go to the studio and professional pride would not let her go back on her word. Promptly at ten o'clock next morning she parked in the crowded car park at Elstree studios and made her way to the two-storeyed concrete building where he had his office.

He was seated behind a massive desk, a pair of heavy-framed spectacles halfway down the bridge of his nose. He looked every inch a film mogul, and she grinned.

He rose to greet her. 'I was afraid you'd chicken out,' he said, leading her to a chair.

'You were right to be afraid,' she conceded. 'But I'm here now, so let's get on with it.'

A youngish, slender man came into the office and Bruce introduced him as Gareth Winslow, the art director.

'I understand you want to see the set designs before you do the clothes,' Gareth Winslow said. 'Two of the main sets are already built, and I have sketches of the other ones. If you'd care to come over to the Art Department. . . .'

By the time Samantha returned to Bruce, she knew that if the script appealed to her as much as the sets did, she would find it difficult to turn down the chance of designing the clothes.

'I knew you'd like Gareth's work,' said Bruce, looking at her face and correctly judging its expression.

'Very much,' she agreed. 'Now I'd like to see the full script.'

He handed her a copy and waved her to a chair. 'When you've finished it, my secretary will bring you on to the set.'

'It shouldn't take me long to read.'

'Bart's made a few changes in it since Cornwall. I think he's—well, read it for yourself and see.'

Aware that Bruce did not wish to influence her opinion of the story, Samantha settled back and began to read. After a few pages the characters took hold of her and she became totally immersed in their problems. Yet as she continued reading she became perplexed. The character of Diana, the part which Linda was playing, was quite different from what she remembered.

Samantha nibbled at her lip. She was wrong. Diana had not changed all that much: she was still selfish and egocentric. It was the character of Graham that had been altered. In this new version he was more mature, more able to accept that the girl he loved was not a china doll but a real and complicated person, not always lovable. Samantha wondered why Bart had altered the story in this way. Surely it would have been easier to soften Diana rather than change Graham's outlook so drastically?

Still puzzled by Bart's motives, she went into the outer office to tell Bruce's secretary she was ready to be taken down to the set.

Leaving the main building, they walked along the narrow road which separated one studio from another. They stopped outside a steel door, waited until the warning light above it was turned off—to show the cameras weren't turning—and entered a vast interior that represented a ballroom in an embassy.

A spotlight was focused on Linda, and Samantha experienced a little shock as she saw her again. She had forgotten how beautiful the girl was, and she wondered if she were still pursuing Bart.

'You were quick.' Bruce joined her. 'What do you think of the script?'

'It's a great improvement on the earlier version.'

'I'm glad you noticed the difference. It has far more compassion for Diana, and Graham's not so rigid.'

'Does this mark a change in Bart's writing, or in Bart?' Samantha asked.

'Your guess is as good as mine,' Bruce replied. 'I doubt if either of us will know until his next book comes out.'

Samantha suddenly knew she could not wait for this to happen. She could not go on speculating if Bart himself had changed. She would have to find out for herself. And fast.

'Come and sit down.' Bruce led her to a canvas-backed chair.

The lights around them dimmed and the main arc lights glowed into life. Linda resumed her position on the set and the next scene began.

Samantha began to draw, making notes beside each figure as she completed a sketch. Subconsciously she must have been thinking about the dresses for the film ever since she had read the script all those months ago in Cornwall, for there was no other way to account for the swiftness and certainty with which she made her designs.

One followed another with astonishing ease, and by the time the scene was filmed, ten pages of her notebook were filled. Exhausted by the frenzied concentration, Samantha shakily handed Bruce the sketches.

'I've marked the colour combinations on each one,' she murmured. 'But I'll get Carol to set them out more clearly for you.'

'There's no need,' said Bruce, lifting his eyes from the pages. 'These are exactly what I want. There's a coolness about them that I like, yet they're sexy too. You're a genius, darling. Come into the restaurant and I'll give you some of my special caviar.'

'Another time,' she relied. 'I must get back to London.'

Bruce looked disappointed, but he did not argue, and led her to the car.

'Will you need to come down again before you start making the dresses?' he asked as she took her place at the wheel.

'I won't, but some of my staff will. I'll only be doing the designs—which is the part of the work I love.'

'You're lucky to have your heart's desire so early in life,' he teased.

'I don't have all I desire,' she said.

'Nor does Bart.'

Without replying, Samantha switched on the ignition and eased out of the parking bay. Bruce stepped back and the car gathered speed and shot away.

For the rest of the day and well into the night, Samantha developed the sketches she had begun in the studio. Then she looked through swatches of SAM fabrics and chose the ones she considered appropriate for each sketch. At nine-thirty the following morning she asked Carol to come to the house and gave her all the designs and fabric suggestions.

'I like the line you've evolved,' Carol exclaimed in admiration. 'It's a pity you didn't design all the clothes for the film; you might have got yourself an Oscar.'

'Maybe I will for Bart's next film.'

Carol looked at Samantha in surprise. 'So that's why I

saw a suitcase in the hall? I take it you're going to see him?'

'I'm going to try,' Samantha hedged. 'He's working on a new book and avoiding everyone.'

'He'll see *you*,' Carol said with confidence.

'I wish I was so sure. He was furious with me when we parted.'

'Because he loves you.'

'Or loved,' Samantha said. 'It may be a past emotion—like so many of his other affairs.'

'If he doesn't see you in a different way from all the others, the sooner you find out the better.'

Samantha thought of this as she sat in the plane that was taking her to Nice. She wondered what she would do if Bart had truly stopped caring for her, and almost decided she had made a mistake to come here like this. After all, why should he still love her? She had thrown his proposal back in his face and probably hurt his pride more than any other woman had done.

By the time she stepped out of the aircraft, she was in such a state of tension that she had to treat herself to a stiff brandy before being able to continue on the final stage of her journey, and she remembered little of the drive along the coast road to Monte Carlo.

Bart's house lay in the hills above the town, hidden from the main road by a long winding wall of grey stone. Tall iron gates barred the car's way and the driver stopped outside them. Samantha got out and was about to press the bell let into one of the stone pillars, when she saw a Renault coming down the drive towards them, Arthur at the wheel.

'Miss Rose!' he exclaimed when he saw her, and jumped out of the car. 'This is an unexpected pleasure. Mr Jackson never said you were coming.'

'He doesn't know.' Samantha waited as Arthur opened the gates. 'Where is he?'

'Working in his study. He only comes out for an hour's

walk each day and to go to bed at night. It'll be good for him to have you here. It will force him to rest.'

'He may tell me to go straight back to London.'

'I don't think he'll do that, miss.'

'I hope you're saying that from knowledge rather than expectancy?'

'A little bit of both,' Arthur smiled. 'Shall I take your case from the taxi? It will save the man driving up to the house.'

Samantha nodded and Arthur took her case, then insisted on paying the fare.

'I'll walk up to the house from here,' Samantha said. 'You can bring my case up when you come back.'

Sensing she wished to be alone, Arthur returned to the Renault and drove out through the gates.

Samantha went slowly up the drive. It was considerably warmer here than in London, with a softness in the air which came from the nearness to the sea, and a clear fresh smell of mountain grass and trees. The grounds were beautifully tended, and though it was November, roses still bloomed profusely. She glimpsed a swimming pool half hidden by shrubs and, rounding another bend, saw the house. It was two-storeyed and rambling, with a wide terrace on the south side overlooking the coast.

She reached the front door and tentatively turned the handle. The door swung open and she stepped into a hexagonal hall furnished in the old Provençal manner, with beautifully carved chairs and tables, a red-tiled floor and sapphire blue curtains.

The house was quiet, apart from the familiar clickety-clack of a typewriter. The sound increased her nervousness and her heart started to pound. Drawing a deep breath, she walked swiftly towards the room from where the sound was coming, and knocked on the door.

The noise of the typewriter did not cease and she knocked again. Still the typing continued and she opened the door and went in.

Bart was half-turned away from her, facing the window. Whenever he raised his eyes from the typewriter he would have an unimpeded view across the lawns to the magnificent coast that stretched below. No wonder he loved to live here.

'For God's sake leave the tray and go.' Bart's voice was husky with fatigue.

Samantha knew she should run over to him, but her legs were rooted to the ground.

Bart turned his head impatiently, the movement stopping abruptly as he saw her. For several seconds he was motionless.

'Well, well,' he drawled, his voice seeming to sink an octave lower. 'To what do I owe the honour?'

Samantha's lips were dry and she ran her tongue over them. 'I—I'm here because I—I've changed my mind.'

Bart rose from his desk but instead of approaching her, he leaned against the side of it. 'Go on,' he said. 'Tell me why.'

'Because I've been terribly unhappy since I refused to marry you. I wanted to say "Yes", but I was afraid.'

'How come you aren't afraid now? Because you've read the script and thought I'd changed?'

Samantha was so surprised she could not speak.

'Bruce told me,' he went on. 'I rang him this morning to say I was coming up for air and to invite him over for a weekend. He said you were at the studio yesterday and that you were designing the clothes for some of the big scenes.'

'Yes.' She found her voice. 'Yes, I am.'

Bart sat in front of his typewriter again. 'You've had a wasted journey, Samantha. It's too late.'

Although she had prepared herself to hear these words, now that Bart had said them, she did not believe him. It was because of the way he refused to meet her eyes, and the flush that stained the tightly drawn skin covering his cheekbones. Surely he had not been as thin as this when she had seen him in London? Encouraged by her thoughts, she moved over to him and stopped a foot away.

'I know how you feel, Bart, and I don't blame you. You offered me your love and I threw it back in your face. But I was wrong—and cruel—and my only excuse is that I loved you so much that I was scared of what it would do to me if you stopped loving me.'

'What makes you think I won't stop? That I haven't already stopped? Is it because reading a changed script makes you think I'm a changed man?' His smile was bitter. 'You're wrong, Samantha. The writer has nothing to do with the man. What you read yesterday was what my characters believe, not what I believe.'

'You didn't need to alter Graham as much as you did, Bart. You changed him because you yourself no longer see women in such black and white terms.'

'Are you finally giving me full marks for understanding the fair sex?' he asked sarcastically.

'No. You're still too cynical about them. But once we're married, you'll change even more.'

'Except that I've no intention of marrying you,' he said, smiling coldly. 'Marriage is out. Definitely.'

'Then I'll live with you.'

Bart stared at her, trying to gauge whether she was serious.

'Very well,' he replied slowly, 'I'll accept that offer. You'll make quite a lively mistress. But you stay here on my terms. I do what I want when I want.'

'Fine.'

'I won't live in England,' he added. 'So you'll have to commute.'

'That won't be necessary. I've sold my business,' she smiled. 'You aren't the only one who's changed.'

'I haven't changed,' he said stubbornly. 'All I did was to alter a script.'

'If that's what you say, then I'll believe you.' She took another pace and stood within an inch of him. 'Doesn't a man kiss his mistress these days?'

'You aren't my mistress yet.' His arms came out to hold her, their grip strong as iron. 'But you soon will be,' he said huskily. 'I've waited too long for you to waste any more time.' He lowered his face, but before their lips could meet, he drew back. 'No strings, Samantha. You accept that, don't you?'

'Yes.'

'For as long as it suits you,' he finished.

'Of course. How clever of you to guess!'

Not giving him a chance to reply, she pulled his head down till their lips were touching. Though his words had been hard, his mouth was tender, and the fear that had burgeoned within her died. This was Bart as she had always imagined him to be; had always known he could be, once he allowed himself to be free of the past.

'I love you, darling,' she murmured. 'I love you when you're dressed up like an all-conquering male, and I love you even more when you're ill and unshaven and feeling sorry for yourself.'

She unbuttoned his linen shirt and placed her hands on his skin. He sat down abruptly and pulled her on to his lap, the hardness of his thighs telling her the effect she was having on him. She nestled against him, her bones seeming to melt as his fingers sensitively explored her body.

'Don't ever leave me,' he said thickly.

'Never,' Samantha promised, not hearing the voice of the man holding her, but the little boy who must once have said these words to his mother. 'I'll be with you always, my darling.'

'In all ways?'

She blushed and nodded.

'As my beloved mistress?'

She nodded again.

'As my infuriating wife?'

She stiffened, not sure if he was teasing. 'I don't need to bind you, Bart. I'll be quite happy to be your——'

'Liar,' he said, stopping her words with his mouth.

'You've already bound me, little Samantha. I'm tied, trussed and ready to be eaten by you.'

Gently she nibbled his lower lip. 'That goes for me too.'

'Good. So let's make a meal of each other.' He rose, still holding her in his arms, and moved to the door.

'Bart! Where are we going?'

'To have breakfast in bed, what else?'

'But it's four o'clock in the afternoon!'

'So we'll stay there till it's the right time. I've months of longing to assuage.'

Laughing, kissing her, Bart carried her up the stairs.

Mills & Boon Classics

The very best of Mills & Boon
romances, brought back for those of you
who missed reading them when they
were first published.

In
September
we bring back the following four
great romantic titles.

NO FRIEND OF MINE
by Lilian Peake

Lester Kings was her brother's friend, not hers, Elise told herself
firmly. She had never liked him when she was a child, and now
he had come back into their lives the old antagonism was there
still, as strong as ever. Yet somehow she just couldn't stop
thinking about him . . .

SHADE OF THE PALMS
by Roberta Leigh

To Stephen Brandon, Julia was no more than Miss Watson, his
unflappable, highly efficient secretary. A dowdy woman wearing
unfashionable clothes, sensible shoes and spectacles, he would
have thought if he'd considered the matter at all. But he was to
discover that appearances can be deceptive and that there was a
totally unexpected side to Julia . . .

THE BRIDE OF ROMANO
by Rebecca Stratton

It was the charming Paolo Veronese who had got Storm the job
of governess to the little Gino in southern Italy, but it was
Gino's stern guardian, Alexei Romano, who caused her all the
heart-searching. She knew that in getting involved with Alexei
she would be utterly outclassed, but all the same . . .

THE ARROGANCE OF LOVE
by Anne Mather

Dominic Halstad was the most attractive man Susan had ever
met, and made her rather difficult fiancé David seem dull by
comparison. But even if her first loyalty were not to David, what
right had she to think about Dominic — a married man?

The Mills & Boon Rose is the Rose of Romance

Every month there are ten new titles to choose from — ten new stories about people falling in love, people you want to read about, people in exciting, far-away places. Choose Mills & Boon. It's your way of relaxing:

September's titles are:

WHERE THE WOLF LEADS by Jane Arbor
Everybody seemed to behave like sheep where Dracon Leloupblanc was concerned. And why, thought Tara Dryden indignantly, should she add herself to their number?

THE DARK OASIS by Margaret Pargeter
When Mrs Martin's son ran off with Kurt d'Estier's fiancée, she persuaded her secretary Maxine to go off to Morocco to try to pacify Kurt.

BAREFOOT BRIDE by Dorothy Cork
To save face when she found her fiancé strangely unwelcoming, Amy pretended that she was going to marry the cynical Mike Saunders instead — then Mike stunned her by taking her up on it . . .

A TOUCH OF THE DEVIL by Anne Weale
There was mutual attraction between Joe Crawford and Bianca — but marriage, Joe made it clear, was not in his mind.

THE SILVER THAW by Betty Neels
A holiday in Norway was supposed to give Amelia and her fiancé Tom a chance to get their affairs settled once and for all. But somehow she found herself seeing far more of Gideon van der Tolck.

DANGEROUS TIDE by Elizabeth Graham
Her ex-husband was the last person Toni had expected to meet on board a cruise ship to Mexico. But he, it appeared, had expected to meet her . . .

MARRIAGE IN HASTE by Sue Peters
Trapped in a Far Eastern country on the brink of civil war, Netta could only manage to escape if she married the mysterious Joss de Courcy . . .

THE TENDER LEAVES by Essie Summers
Searching for her father in New Zealand, Maria could have done without the help of the disapproving Struan Mandeville. But could she *really* do without Struan?

LOVE AND NO MARRIAGE by Roberta Leigh
Career woman Samantha swiftly fell in love with Bart Jackson, who had no time for career girls and thought she was a quiet little homebody . . .

THE ICE MAIDEN by Sally Wentworth
Just for an experiment, Gemma and her friends had computerised the highly eligible Paul Verignac, and Gemma was proceeding to turn herself into 'his kind of woman' . . .

If you have difficulty in obtaining any of these books from your local paperback retailer, write to:

Mills & Boon Reader Service
P.O. Box 236, Thornton Road, Croydon, Surrey, CR9 3RU.

Masquerade
Historical Romances

Intrigue
excitement
romance

CROMWELL'S CAPTAIN
by Anne Madden

Why should Cathie Gifford, who came of a staunchly
Royalist family, feel compelled to tend the wounded
Roundhead captain? And why should a man like
Piers Denham, who had betrayed his own kind by
fighting for Parliament, be able to shake her loyalty
to the King?

HOUSE OF SATAN
by Gina Veronese

Count Anton von Arnheim's Viennese mansion was
notorious, even in the pleasure-loving society of 1785.
And into it came Eloise, the Count's innocent and
beautiful ward. How long could she go on living
happily in the House of Satan?

Look out for these titles in your local paperback shop from
12th September 1980